Doula Programs:

How to Start and Run
a Private or Hospital-Based Program with Success!

For Linda ~
A Special Woman!
Pauly Perez
3/27/98

Paulina Perez and Deaun Thelen
Cutting Edge Press

Cutting Edge Press
415 Bauxhall
Katy, Texas 77450

Printed in the United States

Book Design and Layout by Cheryl Snedeker
Cover Design by Paulina Perez and Lori Ostapchuck
Edited by Connie Livingston

Library of Congress Cataloging-in-Publication Data
Paulina Perez and Deaun Thelen
Doula Programs: How to Start and Run a Private or Hospital-Based Program with Success!
by Paulina Perez and Deaun Thelen
Foreword by Christiane Northrup. M.D.
Library of Congress Catalog
98-092531

ISBN
0-9641159-7-2

1. Obstetrics-popular works 2. Childbirth-social aspects-United States 3. Education-Medical 4. I. Title

Cutting Edge Press books are available at special discounts for bulk purchases. For more information about how to make such purchases, please call 281/497-8894.

Dedication

Our bodies are where we stay. Our souls are what we are.
Cecil Baxter

To
Maureen Dodd
Whose friendship is a constant if my life, whose kindness and humor nourishes
my soul and whose support for my progressive thinking has never wavered.
pgp

John and Colin
Who unselfishly put their needs second so that I could pursue this project.
dmt

Acknowledgments

My thanks to:
Pat Jones for not only being my friend for the past twenty-plus years but for having the courage, commitment, persistence and patience to help our community understand the value of labor support at all births no matter what the setting- hospital, birth center or home.

                                                                              pgp

My thanks to:
Pam Flannery whose devotion to the spirit of birth kept her championing our doula program with tireless energy and whose willingness to impart her knowledge and philosophy has been priceless.
Jeanne Rosendale who has mentored me with both her hands and her heart in every birth we've shared.
Patty Hendrickson for her continual support of every endeavor I undertake and for keeping me motivated and clear.

                                                                              dmt

Our combined thanks to:
Childbirth Enhancement Foundation for permission to use their Ethics and Standards of Practice.
Cheri Grant for allowing us to include samples of the forms from her book, *Labor Support Forms: A Guide to Doula Charting* as well as other doula program forms.
Ana Draa and Crystal Sada for allowing us to include their client contracts in the book.
Patty Hendrickson for the use of her value identification forms.
Cindy Kerbs, Crystal Sada and Ana Draa for reviewing the manuscript.
Kelly Precie for the use of her doula bill proposal.
Dianne Smith for allowing us to use her proposal for a volunteer doula program.
Cheryl Snedeker, Lori Ostapchuk and Connie Livingston who provided invaluable service in the publishing of this book
Sheri Urban for the use of her statement of purpose.
The following contributors for their trouble shooting expertise:
Kathy Bradley--Childbirth Enhancement Foundation
Wendy Carpenter--Professional Doula of Beautiful Births
Noreen Drago--Birth and Beyond
Cheri Grant--M & W Productions
Buzzy Ito--McKay Dee Hospital
Cindy Kerbs--Birth Partners Doula Service
Connie Livingston--Kettering Medical Center
Liz Marshall, Dani Morrison, and Tanya Rable Collins--CHOICE
Susan Martensen--Oakville Trafalgar Memorial Hospital Volunteer Doula Program and Labor Support Association and Registry

Jeanne Ruebelke--Midwest Doula and Education Association
Shirley Wingate--Birth Matters, Inc.

To all those who have helped blaze the trails by establishing doula programs in their own communities

pgp and dmt

Foreword

No one would argue that providing babies with a healthy start in life is crucial to the overall health of society. But all too often we forget that a healthy start for the baby starts with a positive labor and delivery experience for the baby's mother as well as the baby, a process that sets the tone for the mother-child relationship from that day forward. When it comes to evaluating the quality of healthcare, our medical systems have focused almost exclusively on hard objective outcomes such as infant mortality and morbidity. Yet the so-called "soft," more subjective aspects of a woman's labor and delivery experience are equally important for the long-term health of both mother and baby. In the last few decades mountains of evidence have accumulated that document the profound effects that emotions such as anxiety and fear, and their opposite, calmness and serenity can have on the neurological, hormonal and immune system functions that control such things as heart rate, blood pressure, placental blood flow, and efficiency of uterine contractions.

It is clear that how we are born sets up patterns that may have lifelong implications for our state of health and our human potential. Unfortunately, most people, including healthcare professionals, have inherited a culturally ingrained fear and distrust of a woman's innate ability to give birth normally, a belief that has resulted, in part, from observing the adverse birth outcomes that are so common when frightened, anxious, and vulnerable women are not supported and empowered to birth normally. The widespread use of high-tech birth interventions that have resulted from this mindset can and often do undermine a mother's confidence in herself and her body, thus disrupting her and her mate's ability to bond optimally with their new baby and set the stage for potential later problems on a number of levels whether emotional, psychological, or physical. Though the human spirit has in some cases the ability to overcome adverse birth experiences and their consequences, it is much wiser and healthier to prevent their occurrence in the first place by fully supporting every laboring woman.

Happily, we now have all the data and the science necessary to convince even the most skeptical pragmatist that it makes good sense, financially, emotionally, and physically, to create support systems within all birth settings whose purpose is to empower women to give birth in a way that enhances their self-esteem, confidence, and trust in the process of life. These same environments also welcome newborns and imprint their bodies and brains with the idea that life can be a joyful and safe experience. When peace, joy and love become deeply encoded in a baby's cells starting with her or his birth experience, then that baby and her parents will begin life with more built-in resilience with which to weather the inevitable challenges that life always brings.

Doula Programs: How to Start and Run a a Private or Hospital-Based Program with Success! contains everything you need to know to help facilitate the kind of labor support program that results in joyous birth experiences that help maximize a child's potential for a healthy and productive life. Whether you are a hospital administrator, physician, nurse, doula, midwife, pregnant woman, or interested community member, you will find in these pages exactly what you need to know and do to help support and empower the health and creative potential of laboring women and their babies.

Paulina Perez has devoted her professional career to implementing optimal labor support through nursing, midwifery, doulas and doula programs in hospitals and birth centers in the United States and abroad. As a result, she knows every challenge and every triumph anyone is likely to encounter in the process. And she and Deaun Thelen give you the practical solutions you'll need to get started or improve what's already being done in your area. You will learn exactly what you need to know and do to make optimal labor support and the gifts of health that are the result of mothering the mother a reality in your community. Few endeavors in life hold the potential to positively affect the lives of so many.

Christiane Northrup. M.D.
Author, *Women's Bodies, Women's Wisdom*

Table of Contents

Introduction

Do not follow where the path may lead.
Go instead where there is no path and leave a trail.
Muriel Strode

Doulas are rapidly becoming part of the changes occurring in maternity care. This is the time in history when women's voices, and most doulas are women, must be heard. Women think differently than men and can provide an important component in providing maternity care. The voice of the doula will help the maternity care world be a better one as doulas, who bring their own perspective, share in providing maternity care. Change is necessary to keep maternity care vibrant and growing. Remember that a turtle can't move if it doesn't stick its neck out.

Healthcare is definitely making progress in system innovation and doula programs are part of that progress. Hospitals are realizing that innovation, a change that creates a new dimension to performance, is a key element in creating a healthy organization. Quiet competence is no longer enough in providing healthcare; innovations are critical to success. We must be innovative and have the ability to provide comprehensive care. Innovators are people wanting to make a difference by creating doula programs as a component of comprehensive maternity care. Leaders in maternity care today will use the changes in our healthcare system as opportunities and create doula programs, both private and hospital-based.

Those with established doula programs--both private and hospital-based-- are the innovators who are venturesome, have tremendous energy, tolerate risk and are willing to learn. These innovators transcend geographical boundaries and are a very small part of the population. They are ready for accelerated rates of change and are establishing doula programs as another way of clarifying their values and mission in providing comprehensive, individualized maternity care. They have prepared for the change and innovation sets them apart from others. Many others have become early adopters and have relatively new doula programs. As a group, they also have voluminous energy, talk with the innovators, select the ideas they would like to try out and have the resources and the risk-tolerance to do so. They maintain bridges to the outside via innovators. Others are now watching both of these groups of people and some of them will become the early majority. This group of people, approximately one-third of the population, learn from people they know well and trust personally. Their scope is often local and they are less able to take risks than either innovators or early adopters. Another one third of the population are those who will follow the other three groups and are the late majority. They look to the early adopters for signs that it is safe to venture out and try something new.

This leaves about fifteen percent of the population who will always lag behind as they feel that what was done in the past should always be used as a frame of reference.

Those thinking of implementing a new doula program in their community will need to help raise community awareness about the needs of laboring women and the value of doula care. Anticipate that changes in the medical system involve emotional arousal and self-reevaluation which is difficult for some people. Accepting responsibility for changing is part of making a commitment and is frightening to some people. For that reason, anticipate some resistance to this new concept.

You need more than just brains to establish and run a successful doula program. Those with doula programs must get in touch with their emotions and feelings so that they can become better decision makers and problem solvers. Emotional intelligence contributes to achievement.

Being a doula is more than just having a job. The work of the doula must be her passion and vice versa. If the doula does not love her work she cannot hope to please others. She must have an intense focus and be able to concentrate completely on her goal. The result of working in a profession that is in sync with your personal values and your intuitive sense of what is right results in integrity. Truth is when what you know and say and do are all in harmony. This allows you to think more clearly about new challenges and working relationships. This is true for most doula practices as well as the doulas working in them. One can develop their emotional intelligence quotient by acknowledging their feelings; listening to their intuition or inner-voice, and channeling their feelings into constructive communication or action. Integrity is needed to involve or inspire the people about the value of a doula program. Enjoyment is part of one's life work, and is a byproduct of the expression of your talents and abilities. Excellence comes when you mix talent and a caring heart in the work performed. All doula programs should be created knowing that every person has worth and that the program is based on the value of giving, not just receiving. A doula program should be other-oriented and other-directed. This will pay off for you as well as your doula program as any product, service, idea or cause is chosen based on feelings. Afterwards we justify our choices with numbers or facts. It is these emotions that spark creativity, collaboration, and initiative. This will help you tune into yourself, your doula program, and its potential. If your sister doulas and clients feel you are genuinely listening to their problems they are much more apt to trust you. Studies show that trust is tied to profitability so this will benefit the economic outlook for your doula program. A cornerstone of the doula program should be excellence of service. Doula programs give you the chance to use your head, your heart, and your hands in a way that gives to others. The care the mother receives is the product of the program. Every mother cared for by those in the doula program deserves no less than excellence.

Chapter One

So, You Want to Start a Doula Program

I learned early that the richness of life is an adventure. Adventure calls on all faculties of mind and spirit. It develops self-reliance and independence. Life then teems with excitement. But we are not ready for adventure unless we are rid of fear. For fear confines us and limits our scope. We stay tethered by strings of doubt and have only a small narrow world to explore.

William O. Douglas
Former Justice, U.S. Supreme Court

As you start your doula program, remember that leaders who want to spread change must change themselves. Perhaps that will mean learning how to relate to other health care personnel differently. Perhaps that will mean being willing to negotiate with others. Perhaps that will mean learning new skills. You have all that is necessary to change and to develop a successful doula program. Just let all that is inside of you, and your passion for providing childbearing women an empowering birth experience, out in a creative and purposeful way.

Although this book is designed to provide you with the relevant information to start and run a doula program and help you avoid re-inventing the wheel, there are no shortcuts. To develop and run a doula program you, yourself, will have to change. You will find that you will go through the following processes of change identified by Prochaska as contemplation, preparation, action, maintenance and termination. Contemplation is the stage where you think about starting the program. You have identified a problem and now are thinking about how a doula program will help solve it. You will find yourself in the preparation stage when you are ready to do something soon about developing such a program. Action requires the biggest amount of your time as that will involve research, program development and training. Maintenance is where you will do the hard work of running a doula program. Termination occurs when you have reached the goal of having a successful doula program.

In a private doula practice, you will be your most important employee. Because of this, you need to start with an objective self-appraisal. Do you have what it takes to own and run a business? Most doula programs are run by women and according to the latest statistics gathered by the National Foundation for Women Business Owners, female business owners account for 8 million U. S. Business' and employ one out of four workers, approximately 18.5 million people. You will be joining a group of female-owned business owners. The growth of female-owned businesses out paces overall business growth by 2-to-1 and they are more likely to remain in business than the average firm.

Being an entrepreneur means that you are usually upbeat and open to new possibilities. This is demonstrated by your desire to start a doula practice. Entrepreneurs are comfortable with risk and actually thrive on a certain degree of risk. They are organized, can create systems that accomplish their goals, are committed and have a "whatever it takes" attitude. When becoming an entrepreneur and starting a private practice or independent program you might ask yourself the following questions.

- Am I or can I be a self starter?
- How well do I get along with a variety of personality types?
- Can I make independent decisions?
- Do I have the physical and emotional stamina to run a 24 hour on-call business?
- Am I organized?
- Can I establish realistic time frames?
- Can I tolerate interruptions?
- Can I work with a plan?
- Am I willing to do the research necessary to start a successful business?
- Is my drive strong enough to keep me motivated during "down" times?
- How will this affect my family?

Now take all your passion about providing individualized, self-esteem building maternity care and head toward your goal of a successful doula program by doing in-depth research, setting well thought out goals, planning carefully, taking calculated and reasonable risks and leading by example.   At this point, it will help you to remember the words of Teddy Roosevelt when he said, "I am just an average person who works much harder than the average person."

The idea for forming your doula program probably began in a burst of euphoria. To build on the enthusiasm of this beginning, when meeting with those interested in being involved in the project, you might consider mind mapping as a way to get started. Mind mapping is a graphic technique for outlining, planning, and thinking that uses both sides of the brain. Start by writing down the main idea (for example, hospital-based doula program) in the center of the page. You then add related ideas, thoughts and topics by drawing branches from the main idea (for example, doulas, business plan, name). You can use color, sketches, or symbols to highlight the related ideas. You then add other ideas and thoughts that relate to the topics you just listed in the same manner. This graphic technique helps you see the different relationships of all the information much easier than in outline form or by simply listing topics. Do not be afraid to use your intuition. This technique also stimulates the use of the right brain where most of your "Aha!" thoughts come from.   Several studies done at Harvard Business School have found that business owners attribute 80 percent of their success to acting on intuition.   Listen closely when you hear a still, small voice. The voice of the gut is always closer to the truth; gut feelings sometimes tell us about things that we haven't yet consciously identified.

You will need more than just intuition though.   Starting and running a doula business requires countless hours and tremendous energy. Planning may be the most important and most overlooked aspect of the doula program. Planning begins with determining what the needs of childbearing women are in your community are. You'll have greater success if you are filling a need that is easily aroused.   In other words, if your program serves a type of hunger in the community, it will be easier to sell the services of a doula. Even though you know what service you can provide you must also identify the fundamental benefits of the service. Knowing this will help you target your market segment. Do not make the mistake of trying to serve the needs of all segments of your market. Target the type of client you want to serve and focus your service on that market. For instance, do you plan on providing doula services to pregnant teens? Women with low incomes? Women within a certain managed care system? Women who will be delivering at a certain site? Women in a certain geographic area? Women with a certain history (VBAC)? Although your potential clients need to know what services your program will offer, it is infinitely more important for them to know what benefit they will derive from those services. They are much more likely to hire a doula if they know what a doula can do for them.

For those starting independent programs, another tough question to ask yourself is whether you are starting this program as a business or a hobby. A private doula service can be run as a hobby with the intent that if you leave, the program will close. Starting small enables one to start as a hobby with the option of growing into a small business. However, a business that hopes to grow must have a system in place so that it can survive if the director changes. Even with a small business it helps if you start modestly. Don't bite off more than you can chew. It is true that the highest failure rate for new companies is within the first year but the next highest is between the second and fourth years as the business expands. This is one of the reasons that it is so important that you take the time to have a good foundation for the business. Those without a good foundation are the ones that often don't survive as they build on quicksand and do not have a strong underpinning.

When planning on starting an independent, private practice, a private doula program or a hospital-based program, one must also consider the effect of the doula work on your family and children. Being on call 24 hours a day and working unpredictable hours requires that you have support from all those in your intimate personal life. Prior to deciding upon starting a doula business, it is helpful if you sit down with your life partner and discuss each family member's needs as well as their expectations of you. Ask yourself who will supply those needs when you are not there. You need to know if your life partner sees your doula work as a business or as a hobby. Have you thought about being called away during important family holidays or events? It is always better to plan for the worst and have arranged in advance how the situation will be handled than use denial to cope by thinking these issues will not be a problem. Together, you and your family will set realistic expectations for your doula program. For these reasons, many doulas in private practice start by accepting only a few clients per year and expand their practice as their family adapts to the life of a doula.

As you start your new program, ask those around you in both your personal and professional arena how you sound when you start speaking about your program. After they give you their answers, ask yourself the following questions. Do the answers reflect that I am excited about this? Do they reflect that I believe that it can succeed? Entering a new project or business with a lack luster approach does not head one toward success. Having a passion for the program will help ignite that same intensity in those with whom you work as you develop and run the program. If you don't believe fervently in this program, why would you expect anyone else to believe in it? Having an effective vision for your program is one of the most important factors in your success.

Goal Setting

Setting challenges for your program as well as attainable goals will steer you toward enjoying the satisfaction of meeting the goals. Do not be afraid of success. Both short-term and long-term goals should be established. To generate goal setting ideas, decide first on the outcomes you want to achieve. Decide what your main goal is for your program. This will help you build your program by doing what is necessary to get what you want. In other words, start with the end in mind. Your short-term goals should all lead to your long term goal.

When goal setting, determine the needs of your market. Know what women and families having babies want before you begin. Try to include as much of what they want in your service package as possible. This is often the reason that many intrapartum doulas are now adding postpartum doula care to their programs.

A statement of purpose will help with goal setting and can also be used in your marketing efforts. This statement of purpose will identify your beliefs not only about the doula program but about birth. Refer to the appendix for an example of a statement of purpose.

When you have found your passion and purpose, have established one goal, and reached it, then cross that one off the list and set some more.

First Things First

As you decide to start a doula program, familiarize yourself with the research regarding professional labor support. Read as many books on the topic as possible. Essential reading are the books *Special Women: The Role of the Professional Labor Assistant* by Perez & Snedeker (Cutting Edge Press, Katy, Texas), *Mothering the Mother* by Klaus & Kennell (Addison Wesley), *The Nurturing Touch at Birth: A Labor Support Handbook* (Cutting Edge Press, Katy, Texas) as well as the eleven randomized control trials on the topic of labor support. These books and this manual will provide you with enough material to start and run a successful doula program without paralyzing you with information overload.

Results of Research Regarding the Doula

"Speak tenderly to them. Let there be kindness in your face, in your eyes, in your smile, in the warmth of your greeting. Always have a cheerful smile. Don't only give your care, but give your heart as well."
Mother Teresa

Much of the professional research has been done by Drs. Marshall Klaus and John Kennell. Their first research was conducted in Guatemala and published in 1980 and 1986. Subsequent research was conducted in Houston, Texas and published in 1991.

1980 *The effect of a supportive companion on perinatal problems, length of labor, and mother-infant interaction.*
Sosa, et al.   (Guatemala)

	sample size	income level	CBE	labor support
supported	20	low	no	lay
control	20			

37% of original supported group removed for perinatal problems
79% of original control group removed for perinatal problems

	analgesia use	epidural use	labor length	pit augment	c/sec
supported	excluded	_____	8.8 hrs	6%	19%
control	excluded	_____	19.3 hrs	17%	27%

1986 *Effects of social support during parturition on maternal and infant morbidity*
Klaus, et al.   (Guatemala)

	sample size	income level	CBE	labor support
supported	186	low	no	lay

perinatal complications	supported 27%	control 59%
infants admitted to intensive care	2%	7%

rate of perinatal problems among single and married women

	single	married
supported	7%	13.4%
control	76.4%	61.4%

	analgesia use	epidural use	labor length	pit augment	c/sec
supported	_____	_____	7.7 hrs	2%	7%
control	_____	_____	15.5	13%	17%

Drs. Klaus and Kennell continued their research in a project based in Houston, Texas

1991   *Continuous emotional support during labor in a US hospital*
           Kennell, et al.   (Houston)

	sample size	income level	CBE	labor support
supported	212	low	19%	professional
observed	200	low	23%	professional
control	204	low	43.6%	professional

	analgesia use	epidural use	labor length	pit augment	c/sec
supported	21.7%	7.8%	7.4hrs	17%	8%
observed	28%	22.6%	8.4hrs	23%	13%
control	25.5%	22.6%	9.4hrs	43.6%	18%

	forceps	prolonged neonatal hospital stay	neonatal sepsis eval	maternal fever
supported	8.2%	10.4%	4.2%	1.4%
observed	21.3%	17%	9.5%	7%
control	26.3%	24%	14.7%	10.3%

maternal fever   with epidural 55.3%   without epidural 32.2%

Hofmeyr and colleagues in South Africa also studied the role of the doula and its effect on perinatal care. Their research was published in 1991.

1991 *Companionship to modify the clinical birth environment; effects on progress and perceptions of labour, and breastfeeding*
         Hofmeyr, et al.   (South Africa)

	sample size	income level	CBE	labor support
supported	92	low	no	lay
control	97	low	no	lay

	analgesia use	epidural use	labor length	pit augment	c/sec
supported	57%	_____	9.6hrs	8%	12%
control	58%	_____	10.2hrs	10%	14.4%

	2nd dose analgesia	high anxiety scores	BF 6wks	BF flexible intervals
supported	6.5%	51%	51%	81%

control   13.4%   29%   29%   47%
             maternal feelings of coping well
supported   58.7%
control   24%

1989 *Effects of continuous intrapartum professional support on childbirth outcomes*
Hodnett, et al.   (Toronto)

	sample size	income level	CBE	labor support
supported	49	middle	lamaze22	professional
control	54	middle	lamaze25	professional

	analgesia use	epidural use	labor length	pit augment	c/sec
supported	_____	61%	8.9 hrs	43%	17%
control	_____	89%	8.5 hrs	22%	18%

length of labor with 75 women with and 28 women without pain medication (includes 33 with pitocin)

with   17.1 hrs   without 9.9 hr

length of labor for 42 women without pitocin, with and without pain medication
with   14.9 hrs   without 9.5 hrs

mothers who labored without pitocin or pain medication
supported   68%   control 21%
episiotomy rate
supported   68%   control 21%

number of intact perineums
supported   61%
control   85%

participants who attended prepared childbirth classes had higher expectations of control and higher commitment to unmedicated delivery

What is a Doula?

There are two types of professional labor assistants, the doula and the monitrice. Their duties and responsibilities are quite different.

DOULA

from the Greek "in service of"
provides continuous emotional and physical
support during labor and birth but does not use
any clinical skills in her work

Not only does the doula provide continuous physical and emotional support but she also provides the following:

Someone the mother knows and trusts

The continuous presence of another woman/mother

Help to other primary support person or family members

Help for the mother with special needs such as VBAC, multiple pregnancy, high risk situation, single mother, spouse out of town or unavailable, siblings at birth

Adjunct to the nursing staff

MONITRICE

from the French "to watch over attentively and
to guide"
provides continuous emotional and physical
support during labor and birth and also has
clinical skills to assess fetal and maternal well
being

Role Definition

It is crucial to identify not only what those working in your program will do but what they will **not** do. If the doula program is to be successful, it must contain a clearly defined role for the doula. Some members of the birth team may have preconceived thoughts that the doula is only present in lieu of another support person. Some may feel that the doula is not needed if the father or another family member is present. If your program only fills a certain niche, be clear about that. Be sure to clarify which clients will be served by the program (i.e.: teen mothers). Some programs begin working with only one type of client and expand to others as their program grows and becomes well established. When the role of the doula is presented to those working in and with the program, it will be beneficial if the following questions are answered by each individual person involved.

- What will I be doing?
- What will the doula be doing?
- What can I not do?
- What will I be doing differently?
- When will this process begin?
- Who do I speak to if role confusion arises?
- Who will this service affect?

Clarity of Purpose is Crucial

Clarity of purpose is significant to the success of your program. As you begin, be very clear about who you are, what you believe in and what you want. Remember that once you decide what you want, you can learn whatever it is that you need to know to implement your doula program. Your ability to focus on the program and see it through will take character and perseverance, not unlike that required of a woman giving birth. Your willingness to do things that you know are right for mothers, babies and families is part of the courage you will need as you start this new program. To ensure that your program is a success, keep the following in mind. Be passionate about being a doula. Do not neglect family and friends as they are your greatest supporters. Make every day the best you can and always strive for excellence. Learn to negotiate for a win-win situation in all that you do. Celebrate excellence by rewarding yourself as well as those who work with you. Make your dream your reality. Develop a set of principles for a successful professional life as well as a successful doula practice. Ruth Watson Lubic, C.N.M. has developed the following principles in her over-forty year career in maternity care. Consider using her principles as a guideline when you develop your own.

Lubic Principles for a Successful Professional Life

Begin with the needs of the people
Trust your caring instincts
Learn to tolerate uncertainty
Choose your professional colleagues for their caring philosophy
Be aware that the medical model has failed to serve all
Avoid anger as it consumes energy and clouds vision
Avoid bitterness against political opponents
Value the giving and receiving of truth
Base your design for change on the best science possible
Overcome the fear associated with leadership

Market Research

As part of your market research, investigate the resources currently available in your community. What are other childbirth practices (physician's offices, birth centers, midwifery services, clinics) offering? What are their philosophies and practices? What services are other doula programs, if there are any, offering? Learn about all the doula programs, both hospital-based as well as independent, in your community. Look at the following items:

- What services are they offering?
- What do they charge?
- What are their unique features?
- What image do they convey?

- How are they marketing their service?

Now, decide what will differentiate your program from your competitors. Use the library while doing your research. You will find directories, catalogs, indexes and statistical listings there. Many libraries also have a special business reference section where you will find resources such as *Standard and Poor's Register of Corporations, Dun & Bradstreet Million Dollar Directory, Thomas Register of American Manufacturers*, the *Encyclopedia of Associations* and many others. You will also find journals there and they are often the best source of cutting edge information in a particular field.

Identify the special needs of your community. Are services for teen pregnancy or low income families needed? Do VBAC women in the community need extra support?

What Type Program?

Change is the law of life.
And those who look only to the past or the present are certain to miss the future.
John F. Kennedy

There are advantages and disadvantages to both hospital-based and private programs but whichever program is established, it must **meet the need of those in the community.** When determining what type of program is best for you, be sure that you base it on the power of love of birthing women, not the love of power over birthing women. When one enters the other leaves.

As you decide which program to develop, it will help to check the following table.

	Hospital-based Program	Private Program
Advantages	Builds rapport with hospital system	Flexibility
	Doulas on call on a specific time frame	No conflict of interest
	MD/RN support	Can be home based
	Hospital employee benefits	Extended prenatal contact
	Networking base	Provides phone consultations for question and answer support
	Hospital system financial support	Breastfeeding classes and/or consultation
	Helps determine mother's birth needs and expectations as well as partner's participation level	Referral to comprehensive childbirth education classes or may teach cbe classes

Advantages	Provides phone consultations	Standards of practice decided upon by individual doula and her client
	Helps the mother establish a good breastfeeding relationship	Helps the mother establish a good breastfeeding relationship
	Provides lower cost services resulting in cost savings (especially true if program is volunteer)	Has the option of doing volunteer/pro bono work
	Doula does not have to deal with business aspects of a private practice	Doula has great flexibility over schedule
Disadvantages	Limited prenatal contact	On 24 hour call
	Start-up costs and hospital salary(if paid program)	Financial commitment
	Must work within existing medical system; additional program to oversee	Must do own advertising
	Doula work hours may be dependent on hospital personnel	Responsible for all aspects of business (taxes, bookkeeping, advertising, purchasing, etc.)
	High-risk clients	Must arrange own backup
	Possible conflict of interest	Must develop rapport with many hospital systems and personnel
	Standards of practice may be decided upon by the institution	Unpredictable schedule Hard on family

Outsourcing

Some doula programs are hospital-based while others are privately run. Some hospitals choose to outsource their hospital-based program. Outsourcing a hospital-based program provides a variable, not fixed, cost. When outsourcing a doula program it is crucial that the topic of quality be addressed. This can be done in the consulting agreement between the hospital and the program. A formal agreement indicates a serious commitment on both sides. It also carries the possibility of legal action if the promises aren't kept. The agreement should be organized in a consistent fashion and include the following components:

1. A heading that identifies the type of contract
2. An introductory statement that defines the intention of both parties

3.   Commitments of both parties regarding what each party will or will not do; this is the crucial part of the agreement
4.   Restrictions or conditions for the "what if" situations
5.   Signatures of all important parties

Hospitals thinking of starting their own programs must also consider the advantages and disadvantages to the hospital itself. The following chart is of use in this area.

Advantages to Hospital	Disadvantages to Hospital
Additional maternity service	Cost of establishing and running the program
Progressive, comprehensive, individualized maternity care to offer those in their professional service area	Additional program to oversee
Good PR for hospital	Potential communication problems within the program
Reduces interventions	Revenue may not be possible for 1-3 years
Reduces cesarean rate	Potential for resistance to change by existing employees
Reduces costs	

In hospital-based programs, nursing staff should be involved from the very start. **The quickest way to throw up roadblocks is to fail to ask for or disallow input from the nursing staff.** Existing employees feel valued when they have input into this new program as the doula program affects their job. Involving the nurses immediately shows respect for them and their knowledge. If you are working with a doula program consultant this is often part of her role. Time with the consultant where they can freely voice concerns and fears decreases the tension for both the nursing staff and the new doulas.

What is Your Mission?

The future is not some place we are going to, but one we are creating. The paths are not to be found, but made, and the activity of making them changes both the maker and the destination.
John Schaar

Successful doula programs have a mission statement that describes why they are in business, what they provide, who they will serve, and how they will serve them. The mission statement should identify what your business world is.

It should also reflect what the market wants. In other words, what do those in your community need and want. Keep in mind that they might not even know. Your mission statement should reflect what you want and how that fits with your needs as well as the market you serve. This mission statement should impart how you plan to achieve your goals, how you will present yourself, and what you are offering. It should also include how you will get others to help you, how you will anticipate and overcome obstacles, and how you will respond to your market's changing needs and opportunities. This is especially important given the dramatic changes the health care field is undergoing. It is vital that your doula program is insightful and adaptable enough to flourish in any maternity environment.

Independent Doulas and Forms of Business

If yours is to be an independent program, you will need to decide what form your business should take. Your choices are sole proprietorship, partnership or corporation and all have their advantages and disadvantages. Think carefully before you develop a partnership as a partnership is like being married. Choose partners very carefully. If you are thinking of choosing a friend as a partner, consider what effect working together as partners will have on your personal relationship. Partnerships can work but there needs to be a clear division of responsibility up-front to help avoid problems later. Corporations have the advantage of being able to have others invest in your company, and the fact that the corporation is a separate entity. With a corporation there is a liability shield between you and the corporation, and business debts are separate from your own personal finances. There are two main types of corporations, subchapter C and subchapter S with the C corporation being the "standard" corporation. Consider incorporating if your doula program needs the extra trademark protection, if you have significant personal assets to protect, or if you want to avoid the problems involved with a partnership but want to take others into your business.

For most independent doulas, a sole proprietorship is usually the best choice. This simply means that you are one owner and the business is intertwined with you. If your business makes a profit, it is a profit for you and if it incurs a debt, it is yours personally as well. If your business gets sued, you will be sued personally too. Remember that you have complete flexibility but also complete liability.

Taxes

Depending upon what type of business you have formed, you will either file corporate income taxes or your net income will be combined with other personal income and you will pay taxes accordingly. Take this into account when you decide which type of business to form. You will need to study the new tax laws yourself or work with an accountant or tax lawyer familiar with your type business regarding this issue.

Hiring a Consultant

No problem can be solved from the same consciousness that created it.
We must learn to see the world anew.

Albert Einstein

Hiring an expert to help you set up the doula program is of great benefit. In fact, good consultants are said to yield ten times worth their fees. Don't wait until you have a crisis to use the services of a perinatal consultant with an expertise in the area of doula programs. A consultant can help you identify and investigate problems and help you take steps toward solutions as you implement your doula program. She will be able to help you with many issues such as program design, personnel issues, marketing, doula training, and introduction of the program to both the hospital staff and the community. A consultant works best when they address the maternity unit as a whole. They can then help you solve problems efficiently and at the same time eliminate many of the roadblocks in your path. Consultants cannot work miracles. You must be willing to commit the time and resources to work with the consultant and, most importantly, be prepared to listen to the advice they are giving and act on it .

To locate a qualified consultant, start by reading magazines, articles, and books on the subject. Often the authors of that material also serve as consultants. Ask others in the field who have established doula programs who they worked with and why. During your search for the right match for your program, the attributes of a good consultant listed below will be of benefit.

- Expertise in the business of a professional labor assistant and their techniques
- An objective viewpoint
- New ideas
- Low overhead as they are not a permanent part of your payroll

It is important that the consultant helping you develop your doula program be an expert in that field and have the communication skills to work with hospital personnel. She especially must be able to relate and communicate in a non-threatening, positive way to the nursing staff and other members of the medical team. With hospital-based doula programs, it is imperative that the nursing staff be involved in this project from the inception of the concept.

When hiring a consultant be clear about the assignment in terms of resources, budget, personnel and background material available. Ask up-front how much time the consultant (not one of her assistants) will spend with your program. Be very clear about the results you are aiming for. It is important that their advice and solutions be tailored to your specific needs.   Clarify all fees before you start. Doula program consultants will consult with nursing staff about their concerns and ask for input from them. This allows the staff a safe place to voice fears and concerns without supervisory staff in attendance.   The consultant will help clarify the role of the doula and her responsibilities as well as elicit the expectations of the nurses regarding the doula. It will often help to bring the consultant in at different times in the phases of development of your program. For instance, you might bring her in during introduction of the concept to staff, to train the initial group of doulas and your in-house trainer, and then approximately six to nine months after the program has started. This allows for a smoother transition and problems can be dealt with in a pro-active, not reactive manner.

The foundation for a good working relationship with a consultant is setting ground rules, being very clear about the assignment and devising benchmarks to evaluate your progress.   Last but not least, be sure when you are considering working with a consultant that you are willing to empower her to get the job done.

At the end of the project the consultant should present you with a formal report that outlines the problems you face and what is needed to correct them. This will help you identify goals and ensure that your program gets off to a good start.   Let the consultant know if you prefer that the report be presented in a strategic meeting.

Another type of consultant is the business coach. A business coach is part consultant and part mentor. A business coach will be your mentor, advisor and cheerleader rolled into one. Unlike a consultant, they will follow up with you to see if you are meeting your goals and if you are not, discuss why not. They help you work around your existing problems. In a nutshell, a good coach helps you find and implement your own answers to your problems. When hiring a business coach you might try asking the following questions.

- Why are you best qualified to coach me?
- Why do I interest you as a possible client?
- What do you think is most important about coaching?
- How much time and effort must I commit to succeed?

Growth Model

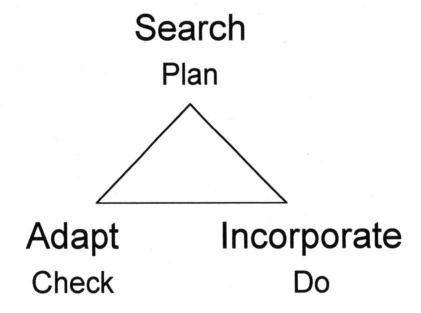

Search
Plan

Adapt   Incorporate
Check   Do

Chapter Two

Will the Program Continue?

The doula program should be set up in such a way that it will survive and flourish if the director is away or the director changes. The following steps will ensure continuity and stability of the program. It is critical that the director of the program know how to delegate responsibility to others. Delegation is important to the long term survival of the program. Begin by letting key people make decisions without approval and putting others in charge for short periods of time. Be sure that there is a strong "number two" person in the program. Sharing responsibility is often hard for entrepreneurs as it goes against their grain but it is important to have an equally strong "number two" person. They add another perspective as well as the availability of a second director when the person in charge is out of town, ill or occupied with other important projects. Utilize experts outside the program who have expertise in doula programs. Developing a board of advisors which consists of two or three trusted people who can help provide input during emergencies or critical decisions also helps tremendously.

Asking Others for Help

Certainty is always a tribute to arrogance. Never be afraid to reach out for help. Using this manual as a guide is one way of asking others for help when developing and running a doula program whether it is an independent practice, private business or a hospital-based doula program. Other ways of asking for help include finding advisors who specialize in the field and using them as consultants. Find an owner of another program to serve as your mentor and help you to develop and implement an advisory board of experts.

Those in independent practice, or interested in starting small programs, can benefit from the new sites for training and counseling women entrepreneurs established by the U.S. Small Business Administration (SBA). These Women's Business Center Programs, part of the welfare-to-work initiative, offer resources women often need to get started in business, stay in business, and expand. This may include financial management, marketing and technical assistance and Internet training. The SBA also operates a toll-tree "Answer Desk" at 1/800/368-5855 and may also be reached online via their web site at http://www.sba.gov/womeninbusiness.

To avoid problems when starting your program, follow the suggestions listed below.

- Avoid automatically recruiting family members and close friends as advisors.
- Be sure that all those involved in the program have mutual goals.
- Include people other than hospital "insiders" on your advisory board.
- Do not try to create harmony by avoiding creative conflict.
- Let your business plan dictate who will be included in running the program.

Another concept that can be helpful is joining with others to do more than you could on your own. Many small businesses and growing companies have partnered with others to improve or develop services or products. According to a survey by Coopers & Lybrand, a professional services firm, these partnerships result in "significantly higher growth rates, larger revenues, more innovative products and greater productivity." You might partner on advertising thus decreasing the costs to both parties. An example of this is Cutting Edge Press, a publisher and retailer of maternity related products, and M & W Productions, a publisher of a labor support forms book, partnering on bulk mailings.

Chapter Three

Plan, Plan, Plan

Use the Internet to do some of your research as well as do business. The number of small business owners using the Internet is doubling as you read this. According to a survey done by the George S. May International Company, an Illinois consulting firm, more than 45 percent of small business owners use the Internet for research, e-mail, advertising and sales. Of those not using the Internet currently, more than half expect to be online within one or two years. Check the Appendix for both software and URL's that may be of help.

Consider having a website for your doula program and put your URL on all your business literature (business cards, brochures, correspondence, advertisements, brochures and Yellow Page listings).

Make your website easy to use. If it is confusing, slow or hard to navigate, you'll lose potential customers. Fill your site with strong content, resources and links to other helpful sites. Be sure that you keep your website current so that people will come back to your website again and again. Consider hiring someone to help design your website if computers are not your forté. Be sure that the computer consultant you work with understands the business you do. Robin Elise Weiss is a computer expert/consultant as well as a doula and can be contacted online at pregnancy.guide@miningco.com. Michael Gandy is a computer consultant who may be able to help you. He can be contacted by mail at HCR 39, Box 322, Morrisville, VT 05661, by phone at 802/888-2969, or by e-mail at progressivecomputing@pshift.com.

Developing a Business Plan

It certainly helps to have business management knowledge and small business experience as you start a doula program but these are not mandatory. You can learn these skills as you plan your program. What you must have as you start though is that fire in your gut to succeed with this new venture.

Writing a business plan is one of the smartest things you can do for your doula program. Do not make the mistake of assuming that you only need a business plan if you are trying to raise money. Business plans help you organize your work by helping you to think logically about the many issues of starting a new business. They help you decide where you are going. It will guide your doula program in both everyday tasks and in growth. A business plan is meant to be a working document and should include the following items: a summary of the plan including the purpose, history, benefits, goals and critical success factors, a description of the industry, a description of the company, a description of the service or product, information on the market, marketing strategy, operations, management of the business, financial projections, capital needs and possibly pictures or price lists. An example of a business plan for a doula program is included in the appendix of this book.

Business plan software is now available and helps you do more than just put words and numbers on paper. This software usually falls in two categories-template-based and full-blown interactive applications. Following is information on nine of the business plan packages on the market. Also included in the appendix is a sample business plan.

Product & Publisher	System Requirements	Program Type	Charts	Average Street Price
Automate Your Business Plan 6.0 for Windows Out of Your Mind...and into the Marketplace 800/419/1513	4MB RAM, 5MB hard-disk space	template	no	$95
BizPlan Builder 5.0 for Windows Jian 800/346-5426	2MB RAM, 4MB hard-disk space	template	no	$89
Business HeadStart 2.1 for windows Planet 800/366-5111	4MB RAM, 10MB hard-disk space	interactive	yes	$49.99
Business Plan Pro 1.2 for Windows Palo Alto Software 800/229-7526	4 MB RAM, 5,5 MB hard-disk space	interactive	yes	$90
Business Plan Toolkit 6.0 for Mac Palo Alto Software 800/229-7526	2MB RAM, 2MB hard-disk space	template	yes	$80

Business Plan Writer 6.0 for Windows Graphite Software 800/659-3030	1MB RAM, 1 MB hard-disk space	template	no	$69
Product & Publisher	**System Requirements**	**Program Type**	**Charts**	**Average Street Price**
PlanMaker 2.0 for Windows Power Solutions 800/955-3337	2MB RAM, 2MB hard-disk space	interactive	no	$99
Plan Write 4.0 for Windows Business Resource Software 800/423-1228	4MB RAM, 4 MB hard-disk space	interactive	yes	$199.95
Smart Business Plan 5.2 for Windows American Institute for Financial Research 800/791-1000	8MB RAM, 24 MB hard-disk space	interactive	yes	$99

One of the leading computer magazines rates the Plan Write 4.0 for Windows 4 stars and recommends it as a best buy for guiding you through creating a business plan. This package steps you through a basic break-even analysis and gives explanations as well as help when writing your plan. There is even an Internet button in the program for access to more than 100 web sites containing tips for the program and ways to improve your program.

The Nitty-Gritty of Funding Your Program

Funding your program will be one of your most important tasks. A hospital-based program or a non-profit, private program may choose to fund the program through grants and foundations. Seek out organizations with funding available. Are there grants available for those working with abuse victims, teenage mothers, low income families, women's issues? A private program may choose to fund the program through donations, volunteer services or private funding. If this is a solo venture, ease into it gradually by volunteering to help other doulas, monitrices or midwives. This will let you "try on" the business of being a doula before you have a lot of financial pressure of running a business. Do your financial research and budget carefully when you do decide to start the business so that you do not end up finding that everything costs three times what you expected.

Applying for grants can often be a daunting process. It will probably take a few submissions to truly understand the process unless you hire a professional grant writer to do the work for you. Knowing your objectives and how to evaluate them will assist you when you need to demonstrate accountability. Read the grant requirements carefully and keep your grant proposal to the point. Establish a succinct budget as you will be asked to justify it in your proposal.

If you are asking family or friends for start-up capital, remember that this money may come with strings attached. Your relationship with these people could be tenuous if your business fails. Even when borrowing from friends and family, draw up a promissory note. Give the lenders approximately ten percent interest; this is still a lower rate than you will get at most banks and lending institutions and shows them that you consider this a business arrangement. You might also seek out those who would be willing to lend you money for a percentage of your business. Investors usually do not want to own the business but, if using this route, arrange a way that you will be able to buy this portion back at a later date.

You may seek a loan from a bank or other financial lending institution. Although this is often what people think of first, do not be surprised if it turns out to be difficult., especially if you have no credit history. When applying for a bank loan be prepared to address the five C's of credit: character, capacity, collateral, capital and condition. If you are using your own private funds as start-up capital you might also consider a home-equity loan. If all else fails, credit cards with low interest rates can be used although you must be disciplined enough to pay this back as if it were a bank note.

If you are working as an independent contractor as you start this hospital-based doula program or are starting a private doula business, you might have your business plan assessed by a counselor at the Service Corps of Retired Executives (SCORE), a federally funded mentoring program (800/634-0245).

Calculating Your Annual Expenses

Developing and using a budget is part of realistic short and long-term planning. Making an accurate, reliable cash-flow projection is important. When pricing the services provided by your business be sure that you have researched what businesses of your type in your area are charging. Doula charges in New York City are quite different than those in Hawesville, Kentucky. You will need to decide if you are going to charge a flat fee, an hourly rate or a combination of the two. You will need to know approximately how much your expenses will be so that you do not find yourself in a cash-flow bind. Your expenses may include the following items: rent, equipment, lending library of books and videos, utilities, service charges for bank account, supplies- both administrative and professional, car expenses, and child care expenses, if applicable.

You will need to have some idea of how many clients you plan to work with per month and what income those clients will generate. Women usually excel at relationship-building which is a vital part of a doula program both in terms of quality and the bottom line but it is equally important to be able to deal with financial issues. An important part of your cash-flow projection is how and when your clients will pay you for your work. This is often the most difficult of all issues for new doulas. For many, it is hard to deal with money issues but if you don't deal with these up front you may not be in business long. When deciding what to charge, look at the average charges for similar services in your community. To avoid undercharging for your services, realize that after you've recovered your expenses each additional dollar helps keep your program in business. As part of your research, pay particular attention to specialized magazines and brochures. See what charges for similar services are being made even in areas distant from yours. Trends in distant markets may reveal information you can apply to your business locally. Charges are also dependent on services offered. These charges may be pro-rated according to ability to pay, may be due at separate times or as a lump sum at a certain time. For instance, some doulas charge an initial consultation fee that is payable at the time of service. When you price your doula services you will need to know how long it will take you to find a client, complete the work and then receive payment. Questions to ask yourself may include the following:

Will I accept a payment plan? Over what interval of time? Will I ask for payment in advance of the birth? Will I require a non-refundable deposit? Will I barter for services? Charges in North America for doula services range from free to $1000 per birth. Many doulas start their business "on the side" and do not initially depend on their program to provide their total income.

Having Trouble with Money?

Determining charges and collecting fees is often a stumbling point for those who have not dealt with this area of business before. If you answer yes to two or more of the following statements you may be having difficulty in this area.

- I feel guilty charging people for what I do.
- I often win new clients on price alone.
- I'm always too busy with work that seems to get backlogged.
- I find myself doing too much "busy" work for my clients.
- I can't afford a vacation or to go to a professional conference.

Initial Costs

Doulas just starting out in business often have difficulty with the financial side of their business. Remember that it takes money to make money. Do not make the mistake of underestimating your initial costs. Be sure to include all the office equipment and services that you may need such as furniture, office supplies, phones and phone services, computers, modems, fax machines, computer programs, scanners and other peripherals, peripheral accessories, copiers, pagers, software and upgrades, service contracts, warranties and tech support. Be sure that they are included in your list of fixed expenses. Track subsequent cash infusions, too, after the initial investment.   Keep a current balance sheet.   Otherwise, your business could be dangerously draining your personal assets. See the appendix for a sample balance sheet.

Learning to develop and administer a budget for your program will help meet and often exceed financial goals. You will use your budget as a "crystal ball" to help you recognize future operating trends. To determine how much money you will need to start up your business the following worksheet will be helpful.

Fixed Expenses

Costs to establish a business identity	name and/or trademark searches, licenses, business structure fees, local permits & up-front research expenses	$
Full time annual salaries	yours, any partners or assistants plus payroll taxes and administrative costs	$
Annual office overhead	rent, security deposits, property taxes, capital improvements, cleaning & trash	$
Up-front utility costs	electricity, gas and phone deposits, installation charges and web site fees	$
Start-up office equipment and supplies	PC, printer, fax, filing cabinet, light fixtures, desk, doula equipment, and office forms	$
Annual benefits/insurance costs	health care coverage, retirement plans, auto and equipment insurance, worker's compensation, employment-practices and liability protection, malpractice coverage	$

All other annual business costs	interest on a fixed-rate business loan, company car loan, professional organization membership dues, etc.	$
Total fixed expenses	add lines 1-7	$

Variable Expenses

Estimated annual taxes	payroll, sales and use, local, state, federal and corporate	$
Annual part-time employee and/or professional fees	training and recruiting costs, accountant and attorney fees, consultant or designer's fees	$
Annual office overhead	Phone (include as special services such as call forwarding, call answering, etc.), electric, gas and Internet bills, postage, shipping and delivery expenses	$
Marketing costs for the year	yellow page ads, Web page, direct mailings, mailing list rentals, business cards, brochures, fliers, newsletters, promotional giveaways	$
Annual travel and entertainment costs	gas, tolls, parking, auto maintenance, conference registrations, client visits, employee events and association meetings	$
Miscellaneous annual costs	bank checks, computer programs, interest rate on business credit cards, interest on mortgage with home based-business, business gifts and charitable donations	$
Total variable expenses	Lines 1-6	$
Total annual costs	fixed expense + variable expenses	$

Previously budgeted?		$
Over/Under Budget for the year	Subtract budgeted amount from total annual costs	$

Keeping a current balance sheet will help avoid overextending yourself money-wise. Know what the financial ratios of your program are as they let you measure and play with the numbers in your balance sheet and profit-and-loss statement so that you can see their relationship to each other. For those just starting out in business, it will be helpful to be familiar with the following terms and their meanings.

Liquidity is the ability to pay your obligations as they come due and still fund your program.
Efficiency is how well your business uses its assets.
Leverage is your ability to borrow money to generate greater return on your investment capital.
Working capital is how much money you have to run your business after you've paid all your bills.
Quick (or acid test) ratio is your most liquid assets divided by your current liabilities (payments you must make over the next 12 months).
Debt-to-equity ratio compares your total liabilities to your equity in the business.
Average days collection is your accounts receivable divided by your sales divided by 365.
Assets turnover ratio is your net revenues divided by your total assets.
Gross profit margin is your gross profit divided by net revenues.
Net profit margin is your net income divided by net revenues.
Return on investment is your net income divided by owners' equity.

Few small businesses bother to gauge whether they're making the most of their economic resources and make the mistake of thinking that number crunching is overkill. It isn't. Most banks will require this information if you are applying for a loan. If you measure nothing else in your business it is critical to measure your quick ratio. Many businesses fail as their quick ratio is below 1:1.
Some costs such as a market research done **before** you start the business must be depreciated or amortized over 60 months beginning on the month you start operating. Failing to amortize these when your company begins means that amount of money will be tied up on your balance sheet until you sell the business.

Home-Based Businesses

According to the American Association of Home-Based Businesses, more than 46 million Americans run home-based businesses for the following reasons: desire for independence; income opportunity; didn't like working for a large company; needed a change; had a great idea; downsized; tired of commuting; and family reasons.

Most private doula businesses are home-based as are approximately 20% of new small businesses. The benefits of a home-based business are obvious:

You control your own time
You have no commute to work
Your rent is reasonable
Increased productivity
Fewer distractions
Being your own boss

There are also disadvantages to having a home-based business. They are:

It is very easy to work too much and too long
Less time for yourself
Hard to separate personal and work lives
Less time for family and friends
Part of your living space must be maintained as a business.

It is important when operating a home-based business that the phone be answered properly. Answer it on the second or third ring or have your answering machine or voice mail system pick up. Don't bring personal details into your business conversations. Train family members to respect that a business is being run from home and try to keep "domestic" sounds out of hearing range of your professional calls. You might consider keeping a mini-script by the telephone for use when answering the phone. Incoming calls are the first way a prospective client gets to know you. Use this to the fullest extent by being prepared and responding professionally.

Permits and Licenses

Research whether you will need a business license for your doula program. This is obtained through your state government. You will need this permit to open a bank account in your business name. You will also need to register your business name in order to open a business bank account. Register your name through your county and they will do a search to be sure that no one else is using the name locally. If you wish to protect use of your business name it may be helpful to consult an attorney who has expertise in copyrights and trademarks.

If you are planning on running a home-based business, be aware that many places have prohibitive ordinances in effect. Contact other home-based business owners in your area or a local or national association of home-based businesses regarding this issue for more in-depth information. Once you are in business, you can deduct from your taxes any expenses associated with starting and running the business. This will include seminars, manuals such as this one, books, professional subscriptions, office equipment, and marketing materials.

Professional Liability Insurance

Liability insurance is one of the issues you will want to consider. If you are involved in a hospital program, the program itself may want to consider blanket coverage that provides insurance for childbirth educators and doulas. Even if you are employed by a hospital program, you may want to investigate private defense insurance, as you are not protected if you give professional advice outside your employment. Do not rely on your homeowner's policy solely and check exclusions carefully. Insurance coverage can cover amounts from $50,000 to $400,000 per incident per year and might also give you portability so you can take the protection from job to job. Liability insurance also provides legal defense coverage, payment for loss of earnings, and future claims against you. For some people, this coverage provides peace of mind. Others feel it adds credibility to their profession, however, you must consider the possibility of lawsuits occurring more easily simply because you have insurance coverage. Going without liability insurance may be a risk you can tolerate, if you do only non-medical procedures.

To get more information about insurance programs for doulas, contact Cotterell Mitchell & Fiffer in New York at 212/233-8911, Maginnis and Associates in Chicago, 800-621-3008 ext. 240, or Dean Insurance Agency in Florida at 407-638-4470. Some insurance programs may require you to join a group or professional association to qualify for coverage.

Spend Smarter

When purchasing office equipment always ask yourself if you can afford to buy this asset. Your yearly projected cash flow analysis will be one of the best gauges. One must know how this purchase will affect the break-even point of the business before the purchase is made. Anything above break-even means the program is making a profit and anything below means it is losing money.   To determine the break-even determine the fixed costs of doing business, estimated revenue, and variable costs. Divide the fixed costs by the gross margin (percentage of income you keep as a profit). If you fall short of this break-even point, delay your purchase.

As office expenses add up, it is important to know ways to save in this area. Start by watching your phone bill carefully, especially if you make a lot of long distance calls. Some people cut long distance costs by switching long distance carriers frequently. You can get a phone rate survey from the

Telecommunications Action Center, PO. Box 27279, Washington, D.C. 20005 by sending $5 and a self-addressed, stamped envelope. Another solution is the use of a new computer program called PhoneMiser. It is a hardware/software combo that scans approximately 20 phone companies every time you dial a call and then places the call with the least expensive service.

Banking fees can often be quite costly. One can compare charges and rates on the Internet at www.bankrate.com (Bank Rate Monitor) which lists CD rates, ATM rates, interest rates, and more. If it is credit card information that you need, check out www.cardtrack.com (CardTrack).

Cutting publication costs when doing your research will decrease overhead. To avoid paying full price for magazine subscriptions, newspapers, and books, do your research on line or at the local library. Cut-rate discounts on subscriptions can also be obtained through discounters. Below Wholesale Magazines (800/800-0062) and Delta Publishing Group (800/728-3728) are two such discounters.

Often, the publishers of magazines may be willing to give you free subscriptions if you pass along "pull out subscription cards" to expectant parents or others who may pay for their subscriptions. They may also be willing to do this if you mention their publications. See the examples of three such publications in the organization resource list in the appendix of this book.

Chapter Four

What's in a Name?

Naming your program is one of the first tasks when implementing a doula program. Choose a name that you can live, grow with and perhaps move with. If you name your program Houston Doula Service and move to Virginia you will need to rename it. This can add hidden costs such as the reprinting of all marketing materials. Be creative when naming your program as your business name is one of your most important marketing tools. It is often the first thing that someone hears about your program. Your business name should be creative, meaningful and imaginative. Flood yourself with ideas from as many people as possible   Although naming a business is not always easy, it can be fun. Use brain storming to come up with as many names as possible in an allotted time (20 minutes). Do not discuss them; simply list them as fast as possible. This helps unchain your brain from habitual thinking patterns while it encourages creative ideas. The name of the business should clearly identify what services the business offers. If someone has to think about what type of program this is, it is likely that they will not call. Make sure your business name is easy to understand and pronounce. Many hospitals choose to use the term doula as part of their program name to identify that the workers provide only nurturing and physical support and not clinical skills which are the province of the registered nurses.   This also identifies it with the ongoing research. Columbia Greenview Hospital in Bowling Green, Kentucky calls their program *Labor Doula Services* while Danbury Hospital in Danbury, Connecticut calls theirs *Danbury Doulas*. The program at Lexington Medical Center in West Columbia, South Carolina is called *The LMC Doula Service Birth Partners.* Other hospitals have chosen the word birth assistant or labor assistant as part of their name to avoid the confusion that can occur between the labor doula and the postpartum doula. John Peter Smith Hospital in Fort Worth, Texas calls their program *JPS Labor Companion Program*. Choosing a name that clearly distinguishes your business from others is important. Your business name will have more marketing value if it is memorable. CEA of Jacksonville chose *Labor of Love Doula Services* for their volunteer labor support program while *Precious Beginnings* is the name of the doula program at Kettering Medical Center in Kettering, Ohio.   Shirley Wingate of Mahomet, Illinois named her independent doula program *Birth Matters* and Molly Bascomm-Keller in Oak Park, Illinois chose *Amazing Births Doula Services* for her business name. The name may also reflect something about the business, perhaps offering a benefit to the laboring woman within the title itself such as *Natural Beginnings*, the business of Linda Worzer, a monitrice in Dallas, Texas, or *Birth Care*, the doula program of Barbara Knox, of White Peaks, Oregon. Just because you understand the word does not mean that the general public will understand the word. On the other hand, having an unusual or unique name can help people remember it, once they have it in their minds but remember that it should also make a favorable impression on those who see it. Sue Coffman of Anaheim, California calls her business *A Doula for Every Woman* and Susan Pearson calls hers **Guardian Doula Birth Services**.

When you have tentatively decided upon a name, evaluate its merits before you make a final decision. Ask yourself the following questions:

- Does this name clearly identify my line of business?
- Does this name distinguish this business from others?
- Does this name make my business memorable?
- Is the name easy to spell and pronounce?
- Can I say this name with pride?
- Does the name include benefits to the laboring woman?

Identify likely clients and test their reactions before you commit to the name. Try someone who you would consider the most conservative client. If it goes over well with them it will probably be accepted by most others. Remember, if you use any name other than your own when conducting business, you will have to obtain a DBA (doing business as) permit from your local government(s).

Chapter Five

The people who get on in this world are the people who get up and look for the circumstances they want, and if they can't find them, make them.

George Bernard Shaw

Telling Others about Your Program: Marketing

Develop an unique selling position (USP). This is the distinguishing advantage you hold out in your doula program. It is the philosophical foundation of your business and should be used in all your marketing and advertising efforts. You must target your clients, project how many you plan to work with each month, and decide how you will generate that level of business.

A marketing plan should be used as a map to more business; it is a set of steps that will help you achieve the goals you have set. Without a well thought out marketing plan you will waste both time and money. This plan does not have to be an extensive one; it can be a page or two that you can post in your office. You may have two marketing plans--one for short term goals and one for long term goals. The short term plan may include things such as getting publicity in local papers and easily fits into the long term plan. Your long term marketing plan which is built on your goals and will tell who you are, what you do, why you do it and how to promote your business long range. The long term plan will help you to project into the future and look at what could happen to the program under various situations. This is especially important with all the changes that are occurring constantly within the healthcare field as a whole. As you write your plan you will be gathering information.

As you begin, take a good look at your program and be objective. It might be helpful to have an individual not directly related to the program give their insights as it is often hard to be objective about something that you have such passion for. Each of you can look at the following issues separately and then compare notes.

- How is your program perceived in the marketplace?
- What is your competition doing?
- How will you attract clients to your program?
- Are the number of clients increasing?
- After the birth, are your clients satisfied with having had a doula?
- Are the doulas working in the program happy?
- How will you measure success?

With your answers to the above questions, you will now be able to sit down and formulate a few short term goals rather quickly to address the challenges and opportunities your program faces. With those goals you can create a weekly timetable for marketing tasks. Break down the tasks into small steps. For instance, collect media contact information one week and send letters regarding the program in the next week.   You might consider using a computer software program in your marketing efforts such as *Marketing Plan Pro* from Palo Alto Software (800) 229-7526.

If you find that you are encountering difficulty marketing your doula program, stop and ask yourself the following questions. Have I targeted a niche for my services? Am I relying just on passive marketing? Do my marketing efforts grab people's attention? What are the needs of childbearing women in my community? Is the market too crowded? Am I excited about my business? The answers to these questions will help you determine what aspect of your marketing you need to focus on.

There's power in the media and it can be used to shape attitudes and influence decisions about health and maternity care. Learn to use the media effectively to benefit not only your doula program but the clients you serve. There are several types of marketing media: person to person; print; direct mail; broadcast; Internet; and billboard.

	Person to Person	Print	Direct Mail	Broadcast	Internet	Billboard
Portability	0	High	High	0	High	0
Cost/Impression	High	Low	Low	High	Low	Medium
Ease of Creation	Easy	Medium	Medium	Difficult	Medium	Medium
Refresh Rate	Medium	Low	Low	Medium	High	Low
Send/Receive	Yes	No-coupon	No-coupon	No	High	Low
Sensory Scope	Verbal/graphic	Print	Print	Audio/Visual	Multimedia	Graphic
Delivery Time	Minutes	Hours	Days	Instantaneous	Instantaneous	Instantaneous
Exposure	Minutes	Sec/minutes	Sec/Minutes	Sec/Minutes	Sec/Minutes	Second
Lifetime	Seconds	Days	Hours	Seconds	Days/Years	Years
Density	Talk	300 words/page	300 words/page	Multimedia	Multimedia	Picture
Receiver Cost	0	0	0	$20-300	$ 3000	0

Talking to the Media
If it takes a lot of words to say what you have in mind- give it more thought.
Dennis Roth

Many healthcare providers have little experience talking to reporters which makes them nervous and fearful of utilizing the media. The best way to learn to cope with talking to reporters is to turn the tables before launching into your first statement. In other words, interview the interviewer by asking the focus for the story as well as who else will be interviewed. Do not start answering questions before you know what the story will be about. When responding to questions, always emphasize the positive. Your goal should be to advance the program or the role of the doula by giving a positive answer to every question. Approach the interview with a clear message. Do not be shy about explaining your experience with the subject; let the reporter know why you are a credible source. This increases the chance that the reporter will call you again when she/he needs information. If you are dealing with television or radio media, the key is brevity. You must learn to explain your program and talk in "sound bites". A sound bite is roughly two sentences that will fill 10-15 seconds of air time. Avoid being misunderstood by reducing the amount of medical jargon you use. Any complicated term is likely to be misunderstood by the media and those listening to the communication. For additional information on how to get on radio and television, consider reading *On the Air* by Al Parinello.

Software marketing programs can help handle marketing and promotions, time tracking and billing, employee scheduling, and feedback received from clients and colleagues. Consult the appendix for a listing of those programs.

For doulas in private practice, person to person and print media seem to be the most affordable options. Hospital-based programs may utilize broadcast media as part of their general marketing efforts. The doula program marketing will simply tie in to their other marketing efforts. For both private and hospital-based programs, it is important to know how to use the media to the advantage of your program. There are several important things one must do. Know the local media (print, radio and television). Let the media know that you have the ear of a significant portion of the community, for instance, women in their childbearing years or pregnant teens. Offer to help by getting to know reporters; letting them know you read or listen to their pieces and sending them story ideas. All reporters are always on the look out for new story ideas.

Visibility with the media has its own risks and rewards. The downside is often the fact that dealing with the media can be risky as you could be the target of a negative piece. The reality is that visibility is a necessary precondition to learning to speak credibly about issues. Obviously, one of the rewards is increased coverage of your doula program and the chance to advance public awareness of an issue that women care about- emotional and physical support during pregnancy, labor, birth and postpartum.

When telling others about the role of the doula, translate objections into questions so that your answers do not sound defensive. As soon as you hear the objection, rephrase it mentally to yourself as a question. Turn the objections into reasons to hire a doula. For instance, if the prospective client questions the price of the doula service counter it with, " Our price is an indication of the value that you will be getting from the doula service". At the end of the conversation be sure that you have heard all the hidden objections by asking directly, "What other concerns do you have about our service?" Eliminate objections with questions. The right questions at the beginning of the conversation helps prevent objections at the end of it. Before you answer an objection, show empathy and understanding for your client by agreeing with her on some point. You have now cushioned your statement with an empathy statement. The person you are talking to needs to know that they have been heard and are understood. Do not be afraid to admit your limitations.

Unlike many other cultures, the role of the doula is new in this culture. Be patient when trying to educate others about doulas and doula programs. Long-lasting success comes from a combination of attitude, knowledge and skill. Taking the time to build a strong foundation in the community will support many years of success.

Cross-promotional marketing via partnerships are also known as strategic alliances. They involve connections with other small businesses as customers, suppliers or local communities. This can help your program stand out in places your competitors can't get to. When considering partnering in any venture, ask yourself the following questions.

- Do they have an equal amount to offer the partnership?
- Do they have resources we don't?
- Is their client base as large or larger than ours?
- Are they willing to sign a agreement/contract that details the partnership and how it can be dissolved if it is not satisfactory?

If yours is a hospital-based program, have weekly or bi-weekly meetings with the doulas in your program to discuss the program. They will be a very important part of your marketing efforts. Occasionally, as a part of your meetings, brainstorm ideas about marketing your program. Have each doula contribute where she has contacts that might help marketing the program. Utilize all opportunities to market your program; discuss your program at professional meetings with colleagues. Contact the professional doula organizations. Utilize their help and support to market your program. Offer to speak at their conferences on the unique aspects of your program. Tap into cooperative advertising in trade publications. Letters to the local newspaper regarding the program can often generate a story; reporters are always looking for new health segments. Keep in mind when you contact the media that you want to be heard, not just listened to. Be informative, not forceful.

Back to Money Again

Be realistic about how much money you can spend on marketing efforts. Use your marketing budget most efficiently. When developing a budget include the obvious costs such as mailings, brochures, cards, ads, transportation and entertainment as well as the not-so-obvious costs such as time spent on marketing tasks. Be unique in your marketing efforts. If you are sending out information about your new program, consider sending them out as a baby gift. You can utilize gift wrap, bows and all the trimmings. This will not only guarantee that your information is opened but read. A doula in private practice in New Jersey has used a very novel way to advertise her services. She goes to the sales office of new home developments and tells them about her business and that it is beneficial information for new families moving into their homes. She leaves them a business card holder with her cards in it and then replenishes it regularly. Doulas who are just starting an independent practice might also want to call local birth centers and other doulas in the area and let them know that they are willing to take clients who cannot afford a doula as a way to gain experience.

If your doula program is hospital-based, you can gain extra support by involving other departments beyond obstetrics and gynecology and childbirth education. The education department, social services, family practice, women's health center and other departments may be able to refer patients to the doula program. Of course, you would want to involve outlying affiliate clinics. Input from these departments may help to alleviate future roadblocks. They may have specific ideas on how a doula service might best be used by certain patient populations.

Network with other businesses whose clients are likely to need your services or whose services your clients need. These might include postpartum doula services, baby stores, lactation consultants, maternity stores, childbirth educators, birth centers, midwives and physicians. Offer to supply door prizes at their events with your business card and name attached to them.

When networking, spend some time figuring out exactly which people can help you achieve your goals and ask them to meet you for breakfast or lunch. If you can't reach the person directly, find a mutual colleague in good favor with the person you want to network with and ask them to set something up. This not only breaks the ice but transfers good feelings to you before you even meet. If at all possible, know something personal about the person you are meeting and ask them about their favorite hobby, etc. as a pleasant opener to the conversation.

Persuasive promotional material should be based first, on the benefits of the program and, second, on the features of the program. In all your marketing efforts answer the potential client's question, *What will this doula program do for me?*

Never forget the number one rule of marketing: **Nothing is more important than following up on all inquiries.** Research shows that the more prompt your follow-up is, the more likely you are to get hired.

Create an Identity

Your marketing material should create an identity for your doula program that lets others know its value, influences their perceptions and communicates information about the program. Avoid having your materials have different typeface, logo and color scheme. This makes it hard for people to identify that the material came from the same company. The identity of your program should be easy for the public to recognize. This can be accomplished by a unified combination of words and symbols that represent the distinctive character of your program.

Business Cards

Many first exposures to your doula program will be through your business card. You want your card to speak to them in as convincing a way as if you would if you were there in person. Your business card gives your program a personality. When designing your logo for the card a cost saving suggestion is to utilize the services of the students in a graphic design class at a local college. They might be able to add your project to class assignments. The small size of a business card and therefore the tight design constraints forces you to decide what information is truly essential. Following are a few tips on business card design.

- Think functional when you begin to design your card.
- Streamline your numbers by listing only your office phone on the card.
- Use call forwarding for your pager numbers when you are out of the office.
- Vary the information on the card based on the audience you will be handing them out to. For instance, perhaps you might want to add your pager number or e-mail address on the cards handed out to your clients. Desktop publishing has made it easy to switch information on your cards.
- Make the type on the card big enough to read (9 or 10 points for the contact information)
- Do not run letters or numbers together.
- Use color or type size to differentiate the levels of information.
- If using symbols be sure that they have meaning.
- Remember that a clean card with lots of white space helps guide the eye.
- Try a vertical card instead of horizontal.
- Decide which information you want to be most prominent and then use bold type face.

- If using color, highlight your name with color.

Telephone Tips

Phone courtesy can make a big difference in both attracting prospective clients to your program and keeping them there. Many people will not do business with people who treat them shabbily on the telephone. Always project a positive attitude even when you're having a bad day. It often helps to gesture as you speak as they translate through your voice. Remind yourself when you speak to be patient and attentive. Find out exactly what the caller needs. If you don't get the right information you can't help them properly. Remember that there is no such thing as a dumb question. Prospective clients need to know that you are approachable. Always return your calls. Nothing will turn off a prospective client more than having to call back and leave messages more than once without a return call. Maintain a professional demeanor even if something is irritating you and always end the conversation on a positive note.

Web Sites

Both private and hospital-based doula programs can benefit from having a web page. First, decide what message you want to deliver on your web page. When writing the page, be concise and state your message clearly. Create a personal feeling with a short bio or pictures. Make sure your buttons look like buttons. If your site includes more than one page, identify each page and include a link back to your home page. Don't include too many complicated graphics as people get frustrated waiting for them to load and may click off your site. Besides your e-mail address, include your mail address, phone and FAX numbers. Be prepared to give your site the care it needs by keeping it updated and accurate. A good example is www.ketthealth.com/precious_beginnings, for hospital-based doula sites.

Generating Referrals

Much of a doula's business is built on referrals therefore it is important to know referral techniques to continue bringing in new clients. This is especially true in a private doula program where the marketing budget is often very small. Doulas excel at building long-term relationships. This trait will help when trying to build the doula program. Building strong, lasting relationships with clients increases repeat business as well as referrals. One-time clients become repeat clients when they know that the doula cares about them and their needs.

To encourage current or past clients to refer others to your business always remind them that you are looking for new business. It is amazing how well this simple tip works in generating referrals.

Even if there is no direct contact between your current and past customers and other prospective clients, you can bring their opinions and satisfaction with your services to others by incorporating testimonials in your promotional literature. Those complimentary letters you get from clients will do more than just make you feel good. Look for ways to highlight excerpts from them in your brochures.

When asking others for referrals, emphasize the value of the doula and the doula program to the client, the hospital and the maternity care system. From your written evaluations from past clients, you will be able to glean comments to use in emphasizing the value of the program. This will help you be seen as more than just someone asking for a referral. You will be seen as a valuable community resource. Offering additional classes besides your doula services is another way to be seen as a community resource. Some doulas are offering classes for fathers on labor support techniques for the father to use. During the class they also, of course, mention the role of the doula and how the doula helps not only the mother but the father too.

It is often helpful to develop a referral reward system where each existing client who refers a potential client receives not only a thank you note but also a small gift such as a parenting book. Clients are usually euphoric after the delivery. Your postpartum visit is an ideal time to ask for future referrals. When someone calls you for referrals to a pediatrician, midwife or obstetrician ask them in return to give your name to others. Cultivate reciprocal referrals from non-competitors by contacting physicians, midwives, childbirth educators, lactation consultants, and nurses. Constantly remind your vendors of your need for referrals. Be sure your name is listed in referral services for the professional doula organizations such as DONA, ALACE and ICEA. Contact them to see what requirements they have for their referrals service. Nationally known doula trainers might also keep a referral list. Paulina Perez, the author of *Special Women: The Role of the Professional Labor Assistant* and *The Nurturing Touch at Birth: A Labor Support Handbook* keeps a referral list for labor assistants throughout North America. Contact the author at 281/497-8894 to have your name or program listed.

Chapter Six

Third Party Reimbursement

Understanding the current healthcare environment is integral to seeking third party payment for a doula's services. Large payor groups such as business coalitions and alliances are willing to channel employees into large integrated healthcare systems (HMO's and PPO's) in exchange for predictable cost and quality measurements. These insurers are competing with each other for contracts. Basically put, a health maintenance organization (HMO) is a risk assumption and management company. Premiums are determined by a community rating system of projected plan wide cost and revenue requirements. These projections are based on expected revenue requirements for individual groups and historical utilization. Therefore, managed care systems are interested in prevention. This fact must be addressed when approaching third party payors regarding reimbursement of doula services. Your aim is to develop a working relationship with the managed care company so that together you can work toward providing quality care at a reasonable cost. For this to succeed, both the doula program and the third party payor must work together.

It is worthwhile to submit a claim for doula services for all births even if you feel that they will not pay. Submit both a copy of your bill and an accompanying letter documenting what the service was, its benefits, not just to the mother but to the insurance carrier, and well as costs savings information. Use the research documented in this manual to show the positive effect of doula care. In the case that your claim is rejected, have your client call the insurance carrier as well as the company that is contracting for the insurance and urge them to reconsider the claim. Again, document the cost savings to both the company and insurance carrier. It is also helpful for the doula to contact the insurance carrier and request that they revisit the claim and mention the cost savings. Know how much money was saved on this particular birth. You will need to know approximate charges in your area for cesarean section, epidural anesthesia, etc. Also let the insurance carrier know that others are reimbursing for this service. Talking to the case manager may also help. Persistence is the key here as well as talking to the person who has the authority to make changes.

Doula services may already be reimbursable depending on how the individual insurance policy is written. The individual doula or the doula program must be able to provide the insurance company with a bill showing the diagnosis, diagnostic code, services rendered, appropriate billing codes, name of individual or program, address, credentials, telephone number, tax ID and professional license or certification number. Insurance reimbursement forms can be designed specifically for your service or may be purchased commercially. Cutting Edge Press carries the universal insurance billing forms of M & W Productions that are available in packages of 100. A listing of common diagnostic and CPT codes in included in the appendix. These will be helpful if you are designing your own forms.

It is also possible to deal directly with the insurance company to have your services listed. One must present them with a package of services designed to promote education and wellness for their subscribers. Assessing, negotiating and securing contracts with HMO's and PPO's is part of the challenges facing those running a doula program whether private of hospital-based. In order to have services reimbursed by state insurance agencies (Medicaid), a similar package can be presented to them. In order to get third party reimbursement for doula services, the program must be able to show the insurance company the following:

The program provides quality assurance.

The program is accountable.

Some doula services have established contracts with health departments (King County, Seattle) and with PPO's or HMO's in their area.

Many individuals have flexible spending accounts as part of their insurance program. Doula services are generally reimbursable under flexible spending plans.

Chapter Seven

Running a Doula Program

Determining the Number of Doulas

The number of doulas for the program will depend on several factors. Among them are: client interest; who will pay for the service (hospital, client, third party carrier); scholarships or grants available for the service; number of births per year to be covered; public awareness and understanding of the program; administrative support; and medical support (nursing, midwifery, physician).

If you are in private practice, you will still need to consider how many clients you will accept in any given month. When accepting clients remember that it is not only the week of their due date that you must be available but two to three weeks before and two weeks after that date. Scheduling more than one client per month demands that you have family support and organization in your life as well as a good backup system in place and excellent child care arrangements if you have children.

When in private practice, not only are you providing labor support to your client but your life partner, family and friends are providing support to you. Everyone involved in this lifestyle must be committed. Yes, having a doula business is a lifestyle not just a job as it entails unpredictable hours, 24 hour call and being away from family for potentially long stretches at a time.

Interviewing Prospective Doulas

Pay attention to the physical changes the prospective doula goes through as you talk with her. Look for a total transformation in the way she looks and acts when she speaks about being a doula and doing something she cares deeply for. When people speak from their soul, it looks and sounds differently than their ordinary conversation.

To avoid potential legal problems during interviews, stick to job-related questions. Focus on the skills of the prospective doula. Do not ask about age, health or marital status. Don't promise job security. If you relate the impression that a job is permanent, you limit your right to terminate a doula. Have an employee handbook that clearly spells out policies regarding holidays, vacations, sick leave, job benefits (health insurance, etc.), and call time.

If you are interviewing for a position with a doula program or with a client, follow the expert advice of human resources experts. Keep in mind the following factors. Learn about the company or the potential client first. Practice for your interview with the doula program or potential client by writing a list of 10 questions that you think they might ask you. Be truthful and do not exaggerate the truth to please the interviewer or client. Be calm and develop friendly eye contact with the interviewer or potential client when you speak.

Hiring Criteria for Doulas

If yours is a private program and you will be hiring doulas you will need to develop an application for employment. A sample of an employment application is included in the appendix of this book.

One of your goals is that your doula program be different than or better than anyone else's so the individuals you hire is of utmost importance. Choose your doulas carefully. Always seek to hire attitude over ability. Invariably, you can educate someone but it is significantly harder to change people's attitudes. You will need flexible employees who can shift from task to task as required. Interview and screen potential doulas with great care. To avoid a high turnover rate, attendance problems and poor job performance it is important that a doula program use a good screening tool when interviewing. This tool can also be used by doulas in independent practice when they are looking for doulas to take call for them.

The application that the prospective doula of a hospital based program utilizes will in most cases be the standard application form used by the institution. Initial interviewing may be done by the human resources department within the hospital, along with reference checks, educational credentials and background checks. The standard list of requirements as maintained by the human resources department should be met for this initial application phase. It is also important to ascertain information about the applicant's prior birth experiences.

Those with private doula programs may develop their own application form and along with hospital-based programs also utilize the guidelines while interviewing prospective clients. Factors to consider during an initial interview include:

- non-judgmental attitude regarding the birth process
- an underlying passion for this type work
- no underlying agenda motivating the applicant to "make-up" for a negative birth
- experience
- warmth and compassion level of the individual
- basic understanding of anatomy and physiology unless this is to be included in your training program
- previous business experience
- barriers to being on a call schedule
- ability to communicate with clarity and conciseness
- ability to set very short-term(2 hour), short-term(24 hour) and long-term(weekly, monthly, yearly) goals
- physical ability to be able to be on feet for long hours at a time
- support system the individual has in place at home
- ability to be spontaneous or "think on one's feet" (Try having them sing Happy Birthday at the interview.)

- professional demeanor
- ability to handle difficult situations and difficult people
- ability to work as part of a team
- flexibility and an understanding of conflict management unless this is to be provided as part of the training program
- comfortable with all the sights and smells associated with the birth process
- willingness to negotiate

It is also important for those running either a private or hospital based doula program to obtain references and educational information. These should be checked. Some programs may want to do background checks as well.

Another option is to purchase an applicant screening survey from a business systems company. Curry Business Systems, Inc. (330/686-7912). offers a screening survey for nursing assistants that could be adapted for doulas.

One comprehensive way to ascertain screening information is by a question and answer format and/or a "discuss the scenario" format. Good questions lead to good answers and the more you learn about the prospective doula the better. Consider including the questions listed below:

- What hours are you available to work?
- Why do you want this job instead of your current position?
- Will this job be in addition to an existing job?
- Do you feel your family will be supportive of your taking this type position?
- Do you have any other education relative to birth that is not on your application?
- Who should make the decisions regarding a woman's birth?
- Who do you think should use a doula? (e.g.: single women, couples, those with no support person)
- Do you feel that you can work effectively with a team approach?
- What strengths do you have that would enable you to provide effective labor support?
- What do you feel your weaknesses are, if any, that might affect your performance as a doula?

Potential scenarios might include:
- A woman you are supporting has been in labor for 15 hours and it appears that there may be several more hours prior to the baby's birth. You realize that you might miss a very important event in your family. What are you inclined to do?
- You are providing labor support for a woman who refuses a hospital procedure such as an IV. What would you do?
- A woman begins to cry during labor, saying that she cannot go on. How do you respond?

- A nurse you are working with seems to dislike your presence. The mother you are supporting begins to notice this. How will you handle the situation?
- A client asks you a medical questions that you are not qualified to answer. How do you respond?
- During early labor the laboring woman and her partner get into a fight about whether to call his mother and tell her about the labor. It is obvious intervention is necessary as the mother is becoming visibly distressed. How would you intervene for the best possible outcome?

Fee Structure for Doula Program

The fee structure for doulas may be handled in a variety of ways. One option is a flat per birth rate. The fee range in North America for doula care ranges from no charge to $1,000 per birth with approximately $300-$400/birth being the average. Monitrices with additional clinical skills usually charge more for their services with $500-$600 being an average fee. Another option is a per hour charge. The national amounts seem to run the gamut from minimum wage to $25.00/hour.

Another option is one similar to the one chosen by Childbirth Resources in Anchorage, Alaska whose doula services charge $425 per birth with a certain percentage of that amount going directly to the doula and the rest to the agency. The client also has the option of paying the agency by credit card.

The doula may also occasionally be paid an on-call fee which ranges from $1-$5/hour with additional payment for holiday call. For hospital programs, their established policy usually determines the on call rate as well as holiday pay rate. In some hospital programs, doulas may be considered "floaters", part-time or full-time employees depending upon the number of doulas on staff and hours required per position. Their wage levels are usually calculated using the criteria of position importance and skill required. Many hospital-based doulas are paid salaries that are equivalent to nursing assistants.

If a doula is an independent-contractor, the program can avoid obligations for state and federal employment tax and wage withholding, employee benefit and pension costs, and compliance with workers' compensations and state rules regarding the workplace. If doulas are going to be paid as independent contractors, the program needs to know how to secure independent -contractor status for the doulas who are not considered employees. The program needs to know the tax definitions of who is an employee, employer and independent-contractor.

Distinguishing an employee from an independent-contractor is made by applying the same criteria used for wage withholding, FICA and FUTA purposes. The following definitions will be helpful to know.

Employer	The person or organization for whom a worker performs a services as an employee *Circular E- Employer's Tax Guide*
Employee	A worker is an employee if the employer has the right to control and direct the worker regarding the result to be accomplished and the details of its accomplishment *Rev Rul 87-41, 1987-1 CB 296*
Independent-contractor	A worker whose work is controlled only in regard to results, and not the means of achieving them *Rev Rul 87-41, 1987-1 CB 296*

The IRS developed a 20-factor control test to make it easier for a business to decide whether a worker is an employee or an independent-contractor. If desired, the doula program may obtain an advance determination by the IRS regarding status of a worker or class of workers for wage withholding, FICA and FUTA purposes. Following are the factors that are guidelines that indicate whether a doula program has sufficient control over a worker to establish an employer-employee relationship. A doula may be found to be an employee if:

1. The doula program directs where, when and how work is to be done.
2. The doula program provides or requires training for a doula.
3. The doula's services are integrated into the operations of a business.
4. The doula's services must be rendered personally.
5. The doula program hires, supervises and pays the doula's assistants, if there are any.
6. There is an continuing relationship between a doula business and the doula.
7. The doula program sets the hours of work for a doula.
8. A doula must work full-time for the program, thus restricting her from doing other gainful work.
9. The work of the doula must be performed on the program's premises or the doula is subject to program control regarding route, territory, etc.
10. Services must be performed in the order or sequence set by the doula program.
11. The doula must submit regular oral or written reports.
12. The doula program pays the doula by the hour, week or month (as opposed to pay by the job or on straight commission) if periodic payment

is more than a convenient way of paying a lump sum agreed upon as a job's cost.

13. The doula program pays the doula's travel or business expenses.
14. The doula program furnishes sufficient tools, materials or other equipment.
15. The doula program has the right to discharge the doula at will.
16. The doula can end the relationship with the program at any time without incurring liability.

The doula may be found to be an independent-contractor if she:

1. Significantly invests in facilities that are not typically maintained by employees, although special scrutiny is required with respect to certain types of facilities, such as home offices.
2. Bears the risk of profit or loss from the endeavor for the business.
3. Performs more than minimal services for a number of unrelated businesses at the same time.
4. Makes her services available to the general public on a regular basis.

The doula program should also be familiar with FICA and FUTA codes Sec. 3121 (d)(1) and Sec. 3306(I).

If the doula is considered an employee, the doula program will use Form W-2 (Wage and Tax Statement) to report the salary paid to the doula. If the doula is considered an independent-contractor, the doula program will use Form 1099-MISC (Miscellaneous Income) to report payments of $600 or more for services performed for the program.

Collecting Fees

Fees are collected in a variety of ways. Some programs charge a deposit that is payable on the first visit and the remainder at the time of service. Some have the entire fee due payable at approximately 36 weeks into the pregnancy while others offer the client the option of paying by credit card. In order to receive credit card payment, the doula or doula program must have established credit card services with banks or a credit card service agency.

More Money Issues

If yours is a program other than a sole proprietorship and you, yourself, or others are employees, you must withhold federal and state income taxes, contribute to unemployment and workers' compensation systems and match Social Security holdings. The importance in keeping good records cannot be over emphasized. These records must be able to substantiate your tax returns under both federal and state which include both income tax and Social Security. The type of records needed will depend on what type business your have. Your accountant will be able to help you here.

Record Keeping Questions to Ask Yourself

How will I use this record?
How important is this information?
Is the information available elsewhere in an equally accessible form?

Contract Between Doula and Client

It is often helpful to develop a contract for use in your doula practice. This may be as simple as a form that lists what the doula will and will not do, the obligations of both the doula and the client, the services the doula will provide and provisions for payment with an area for both the doula, the client and her partner to sign. This type form is included in *Labor Support Forms: A Guide to Doula Charting* by Cheri Grant, R.N. See the appendix for examples of other types of doula contracts.

Ethical Considerations in a Doula Program

Ethical considerations include rules of conduct, provision for backup, responsibility to clients, colleagues, other healthcare workers and the profession as a whole. Competency is an important issue in a doula program as there is no licensure to assure this. Many hospitals are requiring doulas to be certified to work in their institution as a way to assure competency. Doula programs, both private and hospital based, should strive to provide proficient care. Communication with other colleagues, clients and professional should always be honest, fair, courteous and respectful. Back-up is a reliability issue and must be determined prior to hiring doulas or beginning practice. For hospital based programs, call schedules may be determined by the doulas themselves or the program coordinator. For those in independent practice, one must decide if you will be on call 24 hours a day, 365 days a year, have backup just in emergency cases, have backup only when you are out of town, or have backup on a regularly scheduled basis. Chances are you will not have to call upon your backup person very often but it is vital that there be at least one person you can call upon in an emergency. Leaving a client without someone to care for her would be unethical. For those in independent practice, finding backup may be difficult especially if you live in an area with where the concept of doulas is new.

When doing research for the first doula book, *Special Women: The Role of the Professional Labor Assistant,* Polly Perez found that most doulas seemed to come from the ranks of childbirth educators. Therefore, talking to childbirth educators in your community should be the first step in your search for backup. Get to know the maternity nurses in your area as many are looking at this role as an extension of their nursing practice. Area midwives often also do labor support and share the philosophy of birth as a normal life experience. Let all of above mentioned people know that you are looking for backup as they may know of someone in the same situation.

When choosing someone to back you up when you are unavailable, ill or out of town you will want to consider the following issues:

- This individual's birth knowledge and training.
- Is this person easily reached?
- Can she be reached by beeper? Cell phone?
- Does she have voice mail? An answering service? An answering machine?
- Does she have small children?
- What child care arrangement does she have?
- Is she flexible?
- What kind of family support does she have?
- Will you be able to call upon her to assist you at a long or difficult birth?
- Will she meet all of your clients? How? Where? When?
- Will she coordinate vacation schedules with you?
- What financial arrangement will you make for paying her?
  Fee splitting? Hourly pay? Is there a cap on the pay?

All of these things must be agreed upon in advance for your client's sake and that of you and your backup.

Working with others in a business relationship is a large part of being a doula and should be addressed either in the training session or elsewhere. There will always be differences between those who take call for each other and potential problems maybe indicated by the following:

- One person always acquiesces to the other.
- One person believes that the other is not "pulling their weight."
- One person keeps secrets from another.
- One person is focused on the other's faults or mistakes.
- Arguing often.
- Uncertainty about trusting the other person.
- Uncertainty about reliability of the other person.
- Avoiding the other person.
- Feeling you do not need the other person's input on key decisions.

In order to work with others, one must know themselves and their own strengths and weaknesses. If you can't be truthful to yourself, how can you be truthful to your partners and clients? A successful working relationship allows each person to play off the other's strengths. Meeting regularly and talking often helps prevent break downs in communication. It also allows you to update each other and do problem solving together.

If you do all these things and problems within the working relationship still exist, call on a independent third party who can more easily see beyond emotional issues. Depending upon the problem involved, this might be a friend, therapist, lawyer or business consultant.

Doulas as Advocates

Advocacy is part of doula care. As noted in *Special Women: The Role of the Professional Labor Assistant,* advocacy does not mean taking over for the woman or couple and making decisions for them or controlling them; it means helping women or couples help themselves by providing them with information and advice. She (the advocate) makes sure they are aware of their options so they can make informed choices.

It is important that the doula understand the difference in being responsible **to** others and being responsible **for** others as she is responsible to her clients but not responsible for them.

When you feel responsible **to** others...
You show empathy, encourage, share, confront, level, are sensitive, listen.
You feel relaxed, free, aware, high self-esteem.
You are concerned with relating person to person, feelings, and the person.
You are a helper/guide.
You expect the person to be responsible for themselves and their actions.
You can trust and let go.

When you feel responsible **for** others...
You fix, protect, rescue, control, carry their feelings, don't listen.
You feel tired, anxious, fearful, liable.
You are concerned with the solution, answers, circumstances, being right, details.
You are a manipulator.
You expect the person to live up to your expectations.

What to Wear

Whether the doulas in the program are paid or are volunteers or are functioning as independent practitioners, a decision will need to be made regarding their attire at a birth. "Street clothes" may not be the wisest choice as often times labor and birth may provide the need for a very washable garment. Safety reasons (hospital nursery security) and OSHA requirements are also a factor. In a hospital based program, if the doula is dressed in the identifying scrub of the maternity floor, this may heighten her credibility in being viewed as "one of the team." However, a drawback to this may be lab personnel or other individuals assuming that she is an R.N. This problem could be alleviated by wearing a distinguishing badge or other addition to the garment, perhaps a different color stripe or armband.

Private programs often choose scrubs as attire that identify them as professionals but not of the hospital and also sometimes wear name badges identifying themselves as doulas. The advantage of this is the ability to have a set or two of clothes that are for work only, are always clean, and ready to wear. Independent doulas may choose tee shirts that identify them as a doula or their own choice of scrubs which are separate from hospital or other doula program attire. Another option for independent doulas is to wear a scrub jacket over their street clothes. Although some independent doulas feel that wearing any hospital type attire (scrubs, jackets, etc.) might make them be seen as "one of the hospital," others find that the potential for hospital personnel seeing them in a more professional manner was ultimately of greater benefit to the laboring mother. It is often amazing how something so simple creates such a dramatic change in how hospital personnel treat the doula and thus enable her to be of more help to the laboring woman.

Nametags

Nametags identifying yourself as a doula are helpful when working inside a hospital environment. Doulas of North America provides all their certified doulas a nametag upon completion of their certification that shows their name and their certification. When choosing nametags, be sure that the edges of the tag are rounded so that they don't hurt the laboring mother when the doula is working closely with her. Others have solved this problem by having their name and title embroidered on their scrubs or scrub jacket.

Doula Program Code of Ethics

All doula programs, whether private or hospital based, should have a code of ethics as a foundation for their practice. A sample code of ethics for both a hospital based paid and volunteer doula programs as well as a non-profit volunteer program are included in the appendix of this book as well as the code of ethics from Doulas of North America. The conduct of the doula should, at all times, be professional and of high standards. She should strive to have a wide repertoire of skills and continue to build on them via continuing education in the field. A professional demeanor is critical to her practice and her actions should be honest and honorable. Her primary interest and responsibility should always be to her client. Her efforts should foster self-reliance in the mother and she should urge her clients to take responsibility for their own healthcare decisions. Her work with her clients should remain confidential and not be discussed with others without the consent of the client. The doula has an ethical obligation to continue care once her professional support has begun. She should treat all members of the healthcare team with respect, courtesy, fairness and good faith. If conflicts occur, they should be settled outside of the presence of the laboring woman. The birth room should never be a battleground. She should uphold the standards of practice of the program and all her efforts should advance those who come behind her in the profession. Part of the work of the doula is also to help increase public awareness of the role and value of the doula in maternity care. All her actions should promote the general health and well being of both the laboring woman and her infant.

Prenatal Contact

Prenatal contact is an important facet of customer/patient satisfaction and a benefit to both the laboring woman, her partner, and the doula. The ability to meet one's doula before actually going into labor can help to give the woman a greater sense of peace and well being. This may also help a woman who is feeling apprehensive about her impending labor to feel more safe and in control. It may not be possible for each woman to choose a specific doula (especially in a hospital based system) based on the call schedule, how the program is designed and other factors. It can be possible, however, for the pregnant woman and her family to meet all the doulas on staff in a program. This could be accomplished at a "meet the doulas night" perhaps held once a month. This could also be done in conjunction with a prepared childbirth class or a hospital tour, making it more convenient for the expectant parents. A special community event might also be a place where parents and doulas can meet - e.g.- healthy baby fair. Individual appointments may also be arranged within the confines of the doulas schedule. It is possible for a hospital-based program to allow the client to request a specific doula if that doula is willing to attend the birth even if she is not on call. The doula that is on the call schedule would still need to be paid the on call hours, if it is a paid doula program. All of these extras are part of the continuum of care principal which is the cornerstone of doula services.

Call Schedules for a Doula Program

You will need some system of notifying your doulas when their services are required. You may use a rotating schedule that allows for anyone to be called if they are on a master list of doulas. A more effective approach would be to use an on-call system with beepers which allows the hospital and the individual(s) to know who will be responsible and when. This schedule works best when set up two weeks to one month in advance. Since babies don't consider time off for holidays, a schedule that contains a method of fairness will need to be considered. A promise of higher wages (time and one half) on holidays or a rotating schedule between all doulas may be needed. Another option might be to have the doulas self schedule, where they sign up for certain days of the month including holidays. This allows for more flexibility and happier employees.

Volunteer programs often schedule doulas on weekends as well as during the week. Doulas might have regular schedules such as every Saturday or the first Saturday of every month. One program in Florida has doulas that work regular twelve hour shifts with the option to stay longer if they are involved in a birth at the end of the twelve hours. Scheduling is done by the program coordinator.

How many doulas you will need on the call schedule will depend on several factors other than the number of births and the patient demand at your facility. One of the most important of these is how often each of your doulas is able to work. One hospital may do fine with three doulas, while another needs eight, even though their number of births might be the same. It is advisable to have more than one doula on call on any one given day. This allows for a doula to be on call several days in a row (she may not be called in) and allows for another doula to be ready in the event there is more than one birth at a time requiring a doula. This also solves the dilemma of a doula having to do several births in a row (e.g.-two 20 hour labors would be extremely difficult) . This also takes into consideration illness or family emergencies.

How to Reach the Doula

Being available and easily reachable is pivotal to being a professional doula. Those in volunteer programs need to be easily reachable too even if they work at only scheduled times as they often must be on call for those "extra busy" times that occur in all maternity wards. Having a pager can be both a curse and a blessing to the doula. It allows you to go on with your daily routine while being readily available. The flip side to that is you are reachable by pager everywhere at all hours.   Pagers can be either purchased or leased. In addition to the pager itself, you will pay a monthly charge for services and insurance. The monthly service charge will vary with both company and geographical area. Please note that it may be cheaper if you can pay a yearly rate rather than monthly.

Be sure that your clients know that your pager is to be used for *urgent* calls. Other than urgent calls should be directed to your office phone. It will help to give clients examples of urgent calls and let them know that you will call back immediately. As machines are fallible let the client know that is she has not heard from you within 10 minutes to assume that you did not receive the page and to page again. Most pagers are digital and work in the following manner.

TO PAGE A BEEPER
1. Must use a push button phone- NO ROTARY
2. Punch in the phone number of the beeper you want to call
3. The phone will ring & when the computer answers, you will hear 3 beeps or a tone. After the beeps or tones, punch in the number you wish the person you are paging to call plus the # sign on the phone pad
4. You will then hear 3 more beep tones and a busy signal. HANG UP.

Staff Education

Doula staff education is a crucial part of a doula program whether you are in independent practice of one of many other doulas in a private or hospital-based program.   Independent practitioners are obviously responsible for their own continuing education.   Keep your eyes open for maternity related topics offered in your area by nursing associations, doula organizations, healthcare facilities, and childbirth educator associations.   For private programs, initial education is usually done off-site although some larger programs do have on-site programs.   Hospital programs are usually provided on-site with the program coordinator or a consultant brought in from outside.   Training programs should be thorough and include topics other than doula skills such as how to work within a hospital system, communication skills, conflict resolution, negotiation tactics, and administrative issues.   For continuing education, doulas may attend on-site and off-site continuing education programs.   State, regional and national professional organization conferences are also of benefit.   Refer to the appendix for a listing of organizations that offer conferences with information that is applicable to the doula.

Having input into one's continuing education also serves to empower the doula to become a better provider.   Programs often poll the on-staff doulas as to the areas in which they feel more information or training would be helpful.   In hospital based programs other departments may be called upon to provide continuing education (physical therapy, nursing, medicine).   Topics that might be considered helpful for a doula continuing education program include:

* massage therapy	* aromatherapy	* ergonomics
* acupressure	* zone therapy	* homeopathy
* team building	* conflict management	* communication skills
* nutrition	* newborn care	* breastfeeding
*grief	*STD's	* spiritual aspects of birth
* HIV	* stress management	* postpartum mood reactions

* special situations in labor
    -women with previous negative birth experiences
    -sexual and domestic abuse survivors
    -unsupportive partners
    -single parents

In the beginning stages of your doula program, offering continuing education sessions such as those listed on a monthly basis provides a sense of teamwork and closeness. There are other venues available for doula continuing education such as hospital or medical libraries, hospital research centers, prenatal education classes, postpartum classes, mothers groups, meetings with nursing staff, primary caregivers (midwives, family practitioners, obstetricians, perinatologists, pediatricians, & neonatologists), managed care coordinators or case managers, chiropractors, herbalists, anesthesiologists, nutritionists, aromatherapists, acupuncturists, childbirth educators, and physical therapists. Access via the Internet also provides the opportunity for continuing education via online chat rooms, individual communication, and research of areas of interest.

Protect Yourself

All doula programs should have established universal precautions for the protection of the doulas. Hospital based programs must comply with OSHA guidelines for disease protection. Human Immunodeficiency (HIV) and Hepatitis B (HBV) precautions should be followed by all those involved directly with patient care. Breaks in the skin and mucous membranes are potential entry points for both viruses therefore close attention must be taken to avoid contact with bodily fluids. These barrier protections such as gloves, gowns, masks and goggles may be used to prevent the caregiver from exposure. The clothing the doula wears should either be washable (shoes included) or disposable. Avoid contact with uncapped needles or sharp instruments. The doula should wear gloves when in contact with body fluids as in instances of changing bed linen, patient gowns, and towels, when the mother has ruptured membranes, when she starts pushing, applying compresses to the perineum or handling the unbathed newborn. Hospitals now provide gloves in all patient rooms for use by hospital personnel including doulas. Check with your local hospital to see if they have HIV and Hepatitis B policies, procedures and practice guidelines that you might use.

Standards of Practice

Standards of practice should be developed for all doula programs. Each doula in the program should sign and adhere to a methodology for the standards of practice of the program. Each program must decide upon their standards of practice. When deciding standards of practice, several issues surface including autonomy for the client; working relationship with physicians, nurse and midwives; and protection for the client. Doulas of North America has an established code of ethics and a copy of it is included in the appendix as well as a sample standards of practice for a hospital based doula program.

One of the founders of DONA, Penny Simkin has developed a check list to help doulas determine whether they are functioning within the DONA code of ethics and standards of practice. She asks the doula to ask herself the following questions about the action she is to take or advice she is giving.

1.   Are there claims of specific medicinal or healing benefits from the "remedy" (as opposed to soothing a normal pregnancy or labor discomfort) or claims to correct or cure an abnormality?

2.   Are there any possible harmful side effects?

3. Does the action or advice on this subject require special training, certification, or extra education to ensure safety and proper application?
4. Does this remedy usually require a prescription or supervision of a trained clinician?
5. Is the subject on which you are giving advice usually covered by a doctor, midwife, or nurse ?
6. Might your advice conflict with that of your client's clinical caregiver?
7. Might your action or advice worsen the relationship between your client and her caregiver?

Ms. Simkin advises that if the answers to all the above questions are "No" then the action or advice is probably within the scope of practice of the doula. Not everyone agrees with Ms. Simkin. Others feel that these issues are between the individual doula and her client and must be decided upon within the context of that relationship. Hospital-based programs' standards of practice vary from institution to institution.

Care Protocols for Doula Staff

Care protocols should be developed. The following is an example of care protocols for a doula program.

I.   The doula will provide continuous, non-medical support and comfort measures to the laboring woman and her partner/family in order to enhance their birth experience.
II. The doula will create and maintain a supportive, encouraging emotional environment for the laboring woman and her partner.
III. The doula will model supportive behaviors and techniques for any additional labor support the laboring woman, has, without replacing these individuals in their supportive role.
IV. The doula shall at all times strive to maintain an empathetic, sensitive, nurturing, non-judgmental attitude while being sensitive to the client's needs.
V.   The doula shall help the client transition between caregivers due to shift or assignment changes.
VI. The doula will work in conjunction with other members of the birth team assisting in non-medical capacities wherever it is beneficial for the laboring woman.

If changes occur in care protocols for the doula program, they should be clearly delineated to all those involved with the program. This could be as simple as how to call in an extra person or notification of new equipment and how to use it.

Charting and Record Keeping

Paperwork is usually the least favorite part of the doula program but is essential if your doula program is a professional service, not a hobby. You can custom design your own forms or purchase printed forms. *Labor Support Forms: A Guide to Doula Charting* by Cheri Grant includes the following forms that are of help to the doula: prenatal forms, intrapartum forms, postpartum forms, insurance forms, doula records, doula brochures, income and expense forms. The author allows individuals to adapt the form for their personal use. These forms as well as many other doula-related items may be purchased from Cutting Edge Press, a professional labor assistant owned business (281/497-8894). Consult the appendix of this book for samples of a few of the forms from *Labor Support Forms*.

It is also as beneficial for the doula as for other healthcare providers to have these records in the event they are needed in relation to liability issues. Keeping statistics for your program is vital as it is these numbers that will increase your bargaining power and credibility for your program.

The Postpartum Component

A comprehensive postpartum follow up visit is done following the birth experience. This is usually done approximately two weeks following the birth although that may vary depending upon the mother's needs. Often those involved in private doula programs do a home visit for the postpartum followup. Due to concerns about liability issues, some hospital-based programs are not allowed to do home visits. They then either visit the mother in person in the hospital or follow up with a phone call later. Other hospital-based programs set aside a place for a postpartum follow up visit onsite in the hospital. These visits may often coincide with their postpartum follow up visit with their primary caregiver. This visit is the ideal time for closure with the client. A script of follow up questions can help the doula and the client as they discuss the birth experience. A sample of a postpartum follow up script is included in the appendix of this book. Information gained during the postpartum followup visit should be documented and kept as part of the client's record. A postpartum documentation form is included in the appendix of this book. If necessary, additional follow up visits can be scheduled. Giving the mother a written copy of her birth story is not only appreciated by the mother at this time but often remains a permanent part of the child's baby book. The doula should review her birth log prior to the postpartum followup meeting to refresh her memory of the birth. This birth story, written by the doula, recaps the special moments of birth and often plays a part in the overall satisfaction the mother feels about her birth experience. It can also be just that little extra special touch that sets your doula program apart from others. The story can be written on special or colored paper. The doula should ask the mother for a critique of her services. One might ask "How did you feel that having a doula helped you?" or "Is there something you would change about the way I worked with you?" The doula will want to ask if the mother has any special needs such a referrals to postpartum exercise classes, new mothers support groups, lactation consultants, cesarean support or postpartum depression help. The doula should be sure to let the mother know of her admiration for what the mother did and how she coped.

The aim of the postpartum visit is not only to bring closure to the relationship but to leave the mother with a feeling of accomplishment. Many doulas bring a closure gift to the postpartum visit. Examples of these simple gifts are a hand-painted baby tee shirt, knitted newborn hat, potpourri for the mom, picture frame with a birth photo, or herbal bath salts. Let your creativity run wild as you select a gift. This small gift is often a token of the bond formed between the laboring woman and her doula; a bond that often continues on, well after the postpartum visit.

Working with an Existing System
The feeble tremble before opinion,
The foolish defy it, the wise judge it
The skillful direct it.
Jeanne de la Platiere

When working within another existing system it is important to determine what their organizational system is like. Is it the typical **U** shaped system that works by your reporting to your boss or another department head before you can go back down and address your problem? Or are you able to work in what Wilson Harrell, the author of *For Entrepreneurs Only*, calls the entrepreneurial **X**? In this type system, you are able to go straight from the problem to whoever needs to hear about it. This allows you to involve those who have the most knowledge regarding the solution of the problem. It also avoids the quagmire of "tremendous responsibility but little authority" as you will be dealing directly with those who have the authority.

Those working in volunteer hospital-based doula programs might report to the charge nurse at the beginning of their shift to find out what mothers they will be working with. Since they have not met the laboring mother prior to that time, they then go to the mother's room, introduce themselves, explain a little about the doula program and how they can help the mother. The mother always has the opportunity to refuse the service.

Guidelines for Doulas in Hospital-Based Programs

Hospital-based programs will benefit from having a set of guidelines for the program and the hospital for the doulas involved. The following guidelines were developed by Cheri Grant, R.N. for a volunteer hospital-based doula program.

Support Guidelines

Take care of yourself by eating and resting prior to your shift.
When you arrive at the labor and delivery unit, report to the nurse in charge for your assignment.
Change into hospital scrub clothes in the nurses lounge.
Be sure you are wearing your name badge.
Do NOT take valuables with you; a designated locker has been provided for you.
Ask the staff for pertinent information regarding your client.
Wash your hands and prior to entering the patient room.
Introduce yourself as a volunteer with the doula program and give your name.
Allow the woman to accept you or not.
Ask the client if she has taken any childbirth preparation classes.
Introduce yourself to every hospital staff member you are involved with.
Report an significant changes to the nurse assigned to your client such as ruptured membranes, urge to push, etc.
Keep your attention on the laboring woman; avoid lengthy conversations with others in the room.
Do NOT perform any medical tasks.
Praise the woman's efforts.
Stay with the mother for at least one half hour following the birth; encourage bonding and assist with breastfeeding.
Fill out your record.
When leaving, notify the charge nurse.
Do not discuss patients or hospital business outside the program; confidentiality is important.
If you leave at night, do not hesitate to ask security to walk with you to your car.

Chapter Eight

Your Training Program

Prior to attending a training seminar, the prospective doula should have a good understanding of anatomy and physiology of reproduction. You might make a requirement that the seminar attendees have attended a childbirth education series prior to the doula training seminar or have successfully completed a pretest. A sample of a pretest on anatomy and physiology is included in the appendix of this book.

In any event, whether your doulas are volunteers, paid staff, or independent practitioners, they will need training. Those who will be working as independent practitioners may choose to attend a seminar sponsored and held locally or travel to another area for training. When choosing a training program, consider several factors including the reputation and experience of the facilitator of the seminar, their experience dealing with hospital systems and the topics included in the classes. Hospital-based programs will need to decide on providing training through a certified trainer and/or consultant or providing that training themselves. Comprehensive training should include the following topics. This training usually requires a two to four day commitment.

Topics for DoulaTraining Course

Definition of professional labor assistants/doulas/monitrices
Code of Ethics
Standards of Practice
Care protocol and procedures
Introduction to labor support
Working with other support people
A woman's birth experience and her life
Additional recommended reading
Terminology
Premature labor
Early labor
Active labor
Transition
Second stage of labor
Third stage of labor
Apgar scoring
Cervical effacement and dilatation
Electronic fetal monitoring
Physiology of pain
Pain management
Relaxation techniques
Assessing relaxation

Breathing techniques
Assessment of coping skills
Support skills for labor and birth
Physical and emotional comfort measures
Back pain in labor
Physiological effects of heat and cold
Panic routine
Comfort positions for labor
Role play labor situations and comfort/support techniques
Supplies for your birth bag
Drugs and childbirth
Medications that relieve pain during childbirth
Epidural anesthesia
Spinal anesthesia
Fetal presentations
IV's
Induction or augmented labors
Episiotomy
Forceps-assisted births
Vacuum-assisted births
Complications
AIDS precautions
Triple screen test
The Doula and Cesarean section
VBAC
Special Issues
        Birth in other cultures
        Teen pregnancy
        Infant death and grief issues
Breastfeeding
Bottlefeeding
Postpartum adjustment
Postpartum emotions and postpartum mood reactions
Siblings and the newborn
Newborn characteristics
Newborn exam
Postpartum followup protocol
Patient care coordination
Social work services
Community resources
Pregnant patient Bill of Rights/Responsibilities
Communication skills
Reflective listening skills
Team building
Resolving conflicts

Post test
Doula forms
    Scheduling
    Birth story
Doula self care
Professional labor assistant organizations
    DONA
    ALACE
Unit tour/Orientation (For hospital-based programs)
Evaluations

A complete training curriculum can be obtained from Cutting Edge Press. Call 281/497-8894 for more information.

Time Line for Training Seminar Planners

Time Line	Duties
6-12 months prior to event	Select a committee
6-9 months prior to event	Set a preliminary budget Set a date Book speakers Select location Confirm all in writing
6 months prior to event	If desired, get sponsors to help defray up-front costs
5-6 months prior to event	If desired, get exhibitors Request ceu application information Request ceu information from speakers which includes C.V., outline, objectives, teaching methods, bibliography, and audiovisual requirements Obtain mailing lists Develop brochure Request PR photos from speakers
4 months prior to event	Finish brochure typesetting Print brochures Apply for ceu's
3 months prior to event	Mail brochures with expected return being 5-10% Allow 1-4 weeks for delivery if using bulk mail or 5 days mailing first class

1-2 months prior to event	Arrange media coverage (newspaper announcement and articles, radio spots, TV interviews) Process registrations Send confirmations to registrants
1 month prior to event	Arrange catering or refreshments Make arrangements for audiovisual equipment
3 weeks prior to event	Tour facility Early registration deadline Refund deadline Reproduce syllabus for handouts for seminar

Knowledge Testing

After the training seminar, it is useful to have the doulas complete a self-test questionnaire to assure that they have understood and retained the seminar material.   Refer to the appendix of this book for a sample doula seminar knowlege testing assessment tool.

Chapter Nine

Self-Care and Support

It is important that the program nurture both the business and the doulas who work in the program. Many of the doulas will have young children and the program should help them nurture not only laboring women but their own family as well. Having one's own private business while at the same time raising children requires lots of juggling. Both hospital-based and private programs need to address the challenges of a mother employed outside of the home. If you are working from your home, it can bring both freedom and frustration. It is true that having a home-based business means no more dawn to dusk day care and latch-key kids but it means that you will have to juggle your business life with your family life in the same four walls. The flexibility of a work-at-home parent is often cited by children as a benefit to them even though they too will have frustrations.

Each role (doula, mother, wife) affects the other and the doula must learn to manage the roles and integrate them into her self-perception. How she does this will affect not only her clients but also her family, her health and her children. Balancing employment with family life seems to be more of a problem to mothers than to fathers as mothers seem to spend almost fifty percent more time doing household chores than fathers. Following are some tips on keeping harmony in both family and work:

- Physically delineate your office work space from your home area if your doula program is home-based.
- When running a home-based business, have a office phone line separate from your home phone line. This will help avoid either the children or the business monopolizing the phone. You might also consider having an answering machine or answering service to pick up your office phone when you are having "family time." If this is not possible, teach and rehearse with your children what to do when the phone rings and what to say when they answer it.
- Establish clear cut business hours and let all your clients know that unless it is an emergency they should call during those times. In order to do that, you must make the different areas of your life clear to yourself. You must be clear about what is work time and what is family time. Do realize though that toddlers have no concept of roles and may find it hard to differentiate mom's work from mom.
- Keep a list of neighbors nearby who are, in an emergency, willing to come to babysit during the middle of the night or let you drop your children off at their house.
- Trade child care with another doula or develop a babysitting coop with several other doulas or midwives.
- Try not to yell inappropriately at your children. This is difficult if you have just had a frustrating work-related problem. It might also help to let them

know that you are upset about something so that they do not think that they are the reason for your emotions.

- Let go of unrealistic expectations such as those of being a "super mom." Organization and planning helps the mother/wife/doula regain feelings of control.

Believing You Can Do It

The success of your program may lie in your ability to be bold. It takes courage to start a doula program. Don't let fear hold you back. Be brave and push on toward your goal or as John Wayne once said, "Courage is being scared, but saddling up anyway." To begin with, try to identify any beliefs or emotions that are holding you back and then reverse your thinking process. This premeditated self-talk is often called positive thinking. Your current beliefs were formed in this same way and now you must replace old negative self-thoughts with positive new ones. Learn to control negative thinking. One technique involves saying "STOP" to yourself silently or aloud when you find yourself thinking nonproductive or negative thoughts. When you have identified your most common negative thoughts it is time to turn them into positive thoughts or affirmations. For instance, if you are scared of talking to doctors and nurses repeat to yourself, "Speaking to doctors and nurses is great fun." You are now creating a more effective mental script. Often repeating your affirmations aloud at least once a day is very helpful. Make this a positive life ritual in your life.

Another technique that can be of help in building a confident attitude is to identify the weaknesses that are holding you back and keep a daily log until new habits and perceptions are formed. Start your log or diary by deciding which four weaknesses you will address first. You might end up with a list like this: insecurity, defensiveness, rigidity and pessimism. To convert those weaknesses into strengths make their opposites (confidence, openness, flexibility and optimism) important themes in your life, not just your work. Whenever you do something that reinforces one of your themes during the day, note it in your log or diary with a + sign. You will find that when you are able to get the right themes in your life that they will also be in your work and doula program. Life-changing breakthroughs will often follow using your log in this way.

Another way to use your daily log is to write affirmations in it as what you believe to be true you will create. Write the following statement on the top of every page in your diary, "Our doula program is successful."

To start a successful doula program, you must make a name for yourself within the healthcare community. You must be known as a person who deserves to be there. There are three factors that work together to show that you belong to be there: your physical demeanor and presence, a persuasive communication style and a strategic understanding of how to work within the healthcare system to achieve specific goals. As women do not take up much physical space their physical presence is often less powerful than a man's. To make up for this, think of yourself as a "Wonder Woman" and stand with your feet apart with your hands on your hips. It will make you feel more powerful and able to succeed.

Being visible is a key component in effecting change. Use the steeple gesture when you communicate. To do this, place your hands so that just your finger-tips are touching. This forces the palms apart and makes you take up more space whether you are standing or sitting. It is a very common negotiating posture. Being visible may be hard for some people as it involves putting oneself in the limelight or allowing yourself to be positioned there. This visibility involves risk. According to an old saying, "You must be willing to put your money where your mouth is." When starting a doula program this may be true both figuratively and concretely, especially if this is a private program.

You must be seen as an authority. When you enter a room, try to keep your movements to a minimum as it has been shown that the more movements you make, the less authority you project. Keep your head up, develop eye contact, and keep your chin forward and untilted when you communicate. Hanging your head tends to give you a humble appearance. Relax your shoulders backward whenever you want to communicate with authority. Being seen as an authority figure often puts some women up against an old conundrum: Can a woman preserve her feminine, caring qualities and still be seen as authoritative? This means that each of us individually must understand the origin of the conundrum both culturally as well as apart of our personal upbringing. This sharpens our awareness and enables us to develop a more effective strategy for behavior in a primarily male business environment. Our speech patterns, body language and communication skills must reflect self-confidence and project authority. When meeting someone new, explain what you do first and then introduce yourself as it has been shown that in the first seven seconds of meeting new people, no one listens to what you say. They are busy checking you out visually and have difficulty paying attention to anything aural. This is the reason that one often forgets the names of people they've just met. Do not let others finish your sentences for you or interrupt you. Completion, even of a sentence, leads to self-esteem. One needs to be able to complete their thoughts to be seen as effective. If others begin to finish your sentence for you, increase the volume of your voice as you continue talking. If that is ineffective, hold up one finger to show the person that you are not finished talking. If others interrupt you, use assertive communication skills. Hold up your hand; this usually stops people. You might also try saying that you were not finished with what you were saying.

As a woman, acting authoritatively can often bring up another problem-that of the double standard. If we are quiet or tentative we are seen as ineffective. If we speak out strongly with confidence we are seen as overbearing. When a male exhibits the same behavior he is often seen as innovative and confident. This can lead us into the "I can't win" scenario. This is one of the reasons that, in spite of being over one-half of the populations, women are almost invisible as authorities. There are a few communication skills that may help. Listen to how you speak and what pitch your voice takes as you talk. Many women's voices rise at the end of a sentence which makes them sound like they are asking a question instead of making a statement. This may be part of the reason your suggestions are ignored or overlooked. Remember that the lower your voice is, the more credible it sounds. Practice tape recording yourself talking. When you hear your voice rising at the end of the sentence, start over and repeat the sentence forcing your intonation to lower.

It is tough but not impossible to be seen as an outstanding professional and break into the world of decision making.   The results of your hard work in this arena will be the respect and admiration of your peers and other opinion leaders in the healthcare community.

Chapter Ten

Wisdom and Communication

Conflict is the seed of creativity;
Communication the soul;
Honesty and respect the fertilizer.

A North Dakota farmer

The introduction of a doula program means change for the entire obstetrical staff. Change is very frightening to many people. The topics of fear and change **must** be introduced prior to the introduction of the program. True change can only come from within and this requires an understanding of the need for change. The ideas of the medical and nursing staff must be incorporated into a hospital-based doula program. Decisions about the program that incorporate the ideas of both doulas and the medical staff are vastly superior to the single viewpoint of one person imposed on the rest of the group.

When conflicts arise it is not usually because someone wants to harm the program. Since the doula is the "new kid on the block," it is important for the doula to demonstrate to the medical staff that her agenda is the same as the medical staff- safe obstetrical care. If, indeed, their agenda is different than yours, expose it in a cooperative way. Appearing pleasant lets them know that you are not intimidated and helps divert their energy into a mutually beneficial outcome. Reframing the problem or conflict allows you to maintain integrity in the situation. The framework you use will vary from problem to problem and person to person. Discuss several options for dealing with the situation. Keep in mind that you want to end up with a win-win situation for all involved, especially your client.

Sharing Nurturing Aspects of Patient Care

No manager of a doula program or any individual doula can afford to alienate other clinicians. It is why it is imperative that both the program manager as well as the doulas understand the nursing and medical staff roles, hospital politics and how to work effectively with clinical staff so that the mother has her needs met. This is true whether the doula program is private or hospital-based. Nursing staff can sometimes be resistant to the addition of the doula to the healthcare team. This resistance often surfaces around the aspects of nurturing care. The presence of the doula does not mean that the nurse's relationship with the laboring woman can no longer take on an emotional component. If fact, the role of the doula actually enhances the role of the staff nurse. The doula often acts as a bridge among health team members and the pregnant woman. Surveys have shown that women often view their overall interaction with the birth team as better when a doula is present. When dealing with concern about role confusion it is helpful to learn to look at all issues through the other person's eyes. What is causing them to respond in that manner? Why are they saying what they are? What are they really saying?

One of the most difficult tasks of both program directors and doulas alike is that of remaining client-centered especially when the wishes and desires of the client are not the same as those of the hospital staff. The biggest barrier to being solely a patient advocate is the resistance that will inevitably come from other members of the birth team. Obstetrical care may be controlled by a committee or department head that favors a more doctor driven process, whereby the doctor makes the decisions for the patient by virtue of their perspective on the best possible care for the patient. Occasionally what the doctor, nurse, doula or other members of the healthcare team see as best possible care is in conflict with the laboring woman's view. Throw all these different perspectives into the mix and one can easily imagine how difficult it is to remain client-centered.

Quite often doctors, nurses and anesthesiologists tend toward the "medical model" of birth where interventions are not only considered normal but necessary. A doula, on the other hand, is often most likely to apply natural methods before suggesting the introduction of any medication or medical procedure. This basic difference in philosophy can create tension and hostility between members of the birth team and result in the focus on the laboring woman's wishes being lost.

Resistance to Change

People resist change for several reasons. Often they will ask "Why?" and "How?" If you can answer these questions it is possible to move forward to a place where change can be accepted. People resist due to a myriad of reasons which include fear of the unknown, feelings of loss , indignation, and extreme passivity. Just the presence of a doula is sometimes a conflict. It is important to understand that it is the presence of a new type of caregiver and not you personally that is causing some conflict. There are any number of emotions that people experience when faced with change, especially if it is imposed without choice or input. The initial emotions are often negative which does not mean that they are bad, but eventually will drain energy that could be constructively channeled into positive change. We resist by expressing disbelief, annoyance, disappointment, and hostility. Not fixating on the negative is critical. If we fixate on the negative we become despondent, blaming and will try to sabotage the change. Helping others work through the emotions of change will allow them to move to a place of optimism and acceptance.

People choose to make a change if there is hope of gain and an avoidance of pain. The questions everyone on the birth team must ask themselves are "Which of these reactions will help me?"; "How might my choice impede my dealing with change successfully?"; and "How might my reactions affect the laboring woman and the birth outcome?" As most people want to make gains professionally and avoid pain it is important to give as many chances for input and suggestions as possible for all those involved with the program. This allows all to become clear about the program, develop mutual perceptions and philosophy. It might also help those involved to contemplate the change against less favorable circumstances. It is also helpful to look at the change in the perspective of healthcare in general, in other words, to take a look at the "big picture". Reassess your definition of failure. Identify who you see as "your enemy" or those you are in conflict with. Sometimes this may be obvious and sometimes not so obvious and you might even find that you are your own enemy by having hidden agendas that are at odds with your own goals or those of your doula program. While dealing with change, it is helpful to relive positive changes in your past; do not dwell on defeats.

How We Resist

Disbelief
It's just a rumor.
The program won't last.
They've said this before.
Annoyance
Just when I was getting caught up, this appears.
Avoidance
Maybe I can figure a way out of it.
Disappointment
I don't want to have to work with anyone new.
Blaming
I can't believe they expect us to do this.
Despondency
It's hopeless.
I can't tolerate this.
Hostility
I'll show them what a bad idea this is.
Optimism
This will be great for the laboring woman.
Acceptance
I'll do my best.

Since continuous, consistent care is the hallmark of the doula, it is not surprising that the laboring woman and often her partner become bonded to the woman who is their doula. This is especially true for women who have long and difficult labors. This bonding may result in accolades and thanks to the doula that were once reserved for the doctor, midwife, and nursing staff. When this happens others can become jealous of the relationship the woman has formed with the doula. It is important here to remember that most women view the experience with the entire birth team as more positive, and a doula who is cognizant of that fact can go a long way in making sure that all involved are recognized. It is imperative that the woman know that she did the work of birth as this empowers her. Too often when a woman has just given birth and remarks to her doula or other birth team members that she couldn't have done it without them, nothing is said to reinforce the fact that it was the mother who did the work. When that happens an opportunity is missed to help build the woman's self-esteem and help her claim ownership of the birth experience. An appropriate reply to the "I couldn't have done it without you" comment is, "Thank you. We're honored to have been a part of your birth journey but it is you that did the work-not us."

Feelings of vulnerability often surface from nursing staff as they are often being asked to do more work in less time which results in diminished patient contact. Most nurses got into nursing because of the patient contact and are feeling especially vulnerable during this time of upheaval in healthcare. If the role of the doula is made clear up front, it will go a long way to decrease these feelings of vulnerability in relation to the doula as a member of the maternity care team. Nurses are being asked to care for more than one laboring woman at a time as part of their work load. The doula can never replace the nurse as the nurse has advanced clinical skills that the doula does not possess.   Although the job of the doula and the nurses barely overlap, there are occasions where there may be a cross-over of boundaries. Their skills are complementary and the doula is often the bridge for the nurse as her job calls her to other women's bedsides. Still the resistance to change is powerful. Addressing the "fear factor" in change can help one overcome it.

RESISTANCE TO CHANGE

Fear of the Unknown
What does this mean?
What will be required of me?
Are there new responsibilities and what are they?
Feelings of Loss
Of Identity
I've always been a giving person.
Of Relationships
I won't get to know the patient as well as I'd like.
Of Responsibilities
I used to handle that task.
Indignation
I can't believe this happening to me.
Extreme Passivity
I don't want to learn new skills, form new relationships, or learn new responses.

Undergoing change always increases the chances of conflict. Conflict that is resolved openly and honestly promotes health change and disallows for paralyzing problems later on.

Conflict Resolution

The source of most conflict is lack of communication. To avoid this or minimize complaints, publicize the policies of the hospital and the doula program. Resolving conflicts is part of the work of the doula as well as the business owner. Try to mentally rehearse your day, anticipating any trouble spots that you think might occur. See your self rising to each situation with poise and confidence. Even with advance planning , disagreements are bound to arise in most any situation. The doula must represent her client's best interests which may sometimes differ from the best interests of others. Keep an open mind. When communicating, do not use body language that suggests disbelief or disinterest. Do not raise your voice; this stimulates the fight-or-flight syndrome. Be confident in your position and express it positively. Do not alienate the person with whom you are talking with a hard line position. Navigating conflict is a tricky job but one a doula must learn. Those running a doula program will also find these skills invaluable as they deal with employees, vendors, and other managers.

The number one rule is to stay cool when the situation is heated. This takes patience and self-discipline. Being calm and listening effectively provides the perfect opportunity to get to the heart of the situation. Let people work through their emotions first so they will listen to what you have to say. You must first find out what caused the conflict from their perspective before you can begin the work of resolution of the situation.

Listening

With the gift of listening comes the gift of healing. Listening until someone has said the last words in his heart is healing and consoling.
Catherine de Hueck Doherty

Listening is one of the most important skills of both the doula and the director of the doula program. Take the time to hear what the other person is saying. This sounds easy but often isn't as most people listen faster than they talk. Because of this people often find their mind wandering when they are listening. They begin to worry about what they are going to say and therefore can't listen attentively. It will help if you look into eyes of the person speaking. This will help you to hear the information as well as show the person speaking that you are listening and you care what they are saying. When your eyes move away it conveys that you are losing interest. Use active listening techniques that require you to summarize what it is you think you just heard.

Practice is the best way to improve your listening behavior. You might practice by focusing intently and making mental notes when you are listening to the first 5 minutes of the nightly television news. Listen as if you were going to have to write a report of what you heard.

Active Listening
Non-Verbal Attention
Verbal Attention
Backtrack
Clarify
Summarize
Confirm
Transition to Solutions

Active listening sets the stage for conflict resolution by acknowledging the other person's point of view. Make eye contact and acknowledge gestures. It is important to listen to the words as well as the intention behind the words. This is simply acknowledging what they are saying, not necessarily agreeing with them. Practice listening with your heart, not just your head. Listen fully to what the person is saying. Do not start planning your response while they are talking. Listen without interruption, judgment or advice. After you listen, paraphrase what you heard to assure understanding. Active listening involves statements such as , "So. Dr. Jones, what you are saying is that......"

If someone is using attack behavior your natural tendency might be to attack back. Don't! This only escalates the situation. You might use a statement such as, "You talk first and I won't interrupt. Then when you're done, I'll see if I have any questions."

Always be clear, firm, and stress the positive. Stressing the negative only reinforces bad behavior. Suggest positive behavior instead with statements such as, "I know you're reasonable and we can discuss this calmly."

If you find that you are being criticized don't rush to defend yourself. Again, stay calm and try to listen to what is being said. Pause and think before speaking or answering the question. Summarize what you just heard to be sure that you understand. You might try the magical words, "I don't blame you for feeling the way you do." followed by asking them what they would like you to do.

Turning unhappy people into more approachable people can be accomplished by following a few ground rules. Let the person know that you are sorry that the incident occurred. Ask them pointedly what you need to do to make the situation right. You may be surprised to find they often ask for less than what you had imagined. Thank them for approaching you directly so you can work on solving the problem. Do something extra for them. This can be as simple as writing them a note and offering to take measures so that a similar occurrence will not happen.

Group Behavior

If you find, in a group meeting, that people are interrupting each other and pushing their own agendas it is important to set ground rules. These rules can be creative ones like a business in Pittsburgh uses. They have a small glass animal and one must have the animal in their hands before they speak. They also use "Parking Lot" signs. Others may flash this sign if the ideas being presented are off the main road of the agenda of the meeting. Another technique is to have a chart with three kinds of behavior listed and ask the troublesome person to identify her particular behavior based on those listed on the chart below.

Behavior

Red Light
interrupting
stating opinions as fact
being too aggressive

Yellow Light
presenting facts and figures

Green Light
adding to an idea
asking questions

When communicating with colleagues, other health professional or clients the following patterns may be helpful:
- Speak to the need
- Document the conversation
- Say thank you
- Consider relevancy. What does that have to do with this?
- Realize intent. What are you really trying to say?
- Keep your polarity response in check
- Use an expectant look
- Utilize gentle confrontation

Patient-Centered Care

God protect me from self-interest masquerading as moral principle.
Mark Twain

These philosophical issues as well as the issue of patient-centered care must be addressed prior to and continuously throughout the program when a doula program is part of the hospital system. Patient-centered care can mean different things to different people. In order for the hospital, doula, medical and nursing staff to allow each member of the team their individual responsibility as it relates to the laboring woman, each must be congruent in their perspective of patient-centered care. True patient-centered care occurs when the individual patient is provided complete information of all options and allowed to make their own decisions. While in some situations, decisions will be heavily weighted by the situation at hand, all patients must give informed consent. The key word is "informed." Simply saying "sign here" is not informed consent. A hospital or birthing center that functions in an environment of patient-centered care should have informed consent as part of its mission statement and be one of their top priorities. It should be established prior to the implementation of the doula program that questions from the pregnant woman and her family are welcomed and all members of the birth team are willing to discuss all options. Anything less may mean eventual roadblocks for a successful hospital doula program.

Other issues that must be dealt with when implementing a hospital-based program to avoid these issues becoming barriers to the success of the program include misunderstanding of the doula's role; unwillingness of the nursing staff to share the nurturing aspects of labor care; changes in protocol or standing orders; miscalculation of the doula's impact on the birth; insecurity by the nursing staff regarding job stability; power struggles regarding who controls what decisions; possible attacks to sabotage the program by individuals in opposition to this type of care; and existing staff being given no voice in the implementation of the program. Prevention is always better than intervention. Therefore, it cannot be overemphasized that dealing with these issues during the initial phases of implementing a hospital-based doula program is critical. Being sure that everyone is "reading from the same page" goes a long way toward preventing problems from occurring. It will prevent conflicts threatening the program's existence as well as patient-centered care.

What is a Patient?

A Patient
is the most important person ever in
this practice- in person or on the telephone.

A Patient
is not dependent on us
we are dependent on her

A Patient
is not an interruption of our work
she is the purpose of it.
We are not doing her a favor by serving her
she is doing us a favor by giving
us the opportunity to do so.

A Patient
is not an outsider to our practice
she is part of it.

A Patient
is not cold statistics, she is a flesh
and blood human being with feelings
and emotions like our own.

A Patient
is a person who brings us her wants.
It is our job to handle them profitably;
to both of us.

Smart Practice Customer Service

Chapter Eleven

Assuring that Your Program Succeeds

The doula businesses that have the best chance of success have several things going for them such as general business knowledge, small business experience, management experience, working or technical knowledge, good physical and mental health and a passion for the work. When you are self-motivated and passionate about the work, you are more driven to succeed.

When starting a business, don't be afraid to fail. Spectators never fail; those who are players and run a business often do. Your doula program will never have any failures if you don't start it. See any failures as temporary setbacks or as learning opportunities. Mistakes and success are intertwined. Learn to take smart risks. Those risks involve starting a business you enjoy; overestimating your operating costs, charging the going rate for doula services; never taking the public for granted; maintaining good relations with your banker; hiring a consultant; defining clearly each person's role and responsibilities; understanding the changing healthcare system; joining professional organizations; and becoming certified in the doula profession. Mistakes include: starting the doula program strictly to make money; pretending to have more start-up funds than you really have; assuming that if you charge lower than your competition people will flock to your door; assuming that once you have clients they will always remain yours; spending your working capital down to the last dollar; hiring people with the same background and entrepreneurial spirit as yours; being vague in employees' descriptions and job responsibilities; renting expensive office space to impress others; assuming that you do no need the support of colleagues and friends; working without goals; trying to everything yourself; and launching your doula program and becoming so busy that you do not have time to keep up with the doula industry.

Join the American Home Business Association (AHB) and you will receive advice on everything from tax deductions to billing and financial planning. You may reach the AHB at 60 Arch St., Greenwich, CT 06830 or 800/433-6361. Local Small Business Association offices and state Chambers of Commerce can also provide pertinent information on how to manage a home-based business.

Managing Your Doula Program

The behavior of a manager of a doula program will have a direct effect on the staff's morale, performance, productivity and satisfaction. The director must be strong but willing to handle criticism. She must be a good listener as quite often your doulas may need to use you as a sounding board. Action is not always needed. Directors are often called upon to be mediators. The golden rule of motivation is treat the staff as you would like to be treated. Do unto others as you would have them do unto you. This may sound simple but it is often very difficult to strike the right balance between guidance, respect, incentive and fairness. Trust, loyalty and commitment among workers must be inspired to have a smoothly functioning doula program.

People who actively seek out problems and attempt to solve them early before they become major problems are problem seekers. They recognize the need for change and believe that the best way to deal with change is to anticipate it and not just react to it. Problem seekers research data and understand the implication of the data to the program's future. Problem solvers are those who confront problems and attempt to solve them. Problem solvers rarely anticipate problems but are often quite effective in dealing with them once they are aware of them. When problem solving they identify and diagnose the problem and begin to generate alternatives. They evaluate all options prior to making a decision and then implementing it.

Most people do not like to work for an authoritarian manager described as the "do what I say or I'll fire you" boss. Fear runs this system and its attributes often include high staff turnover and low staff morale. This, in turn, causes a decline in productivity and quality of service. When a well-trained employee quits, the program incurs not only out-of-pocket hiring and training costs but the "opportunity cost" of having a less effective, new employee who will need three to six months before becoming a productive, efficient team member. The long term effects of this system can be devastating not only to the workers and the manager but to the laboring mother and her family.

Try to eliminate your staff's need to second-guess you. Answer their questions before they ask them. This frees them up to tackle all of the challenges of doula work. Address their unspoken fears by clearly delineating your expectations, what resources will be provided to help them do their job, and how to communicate clearly with you. This should include the "where, what, when and how" of exchanges with you as well as what information you expect from them. They should always be told in advance how often the doulas will meet with you both individually and in a group. Be clear with them about whether you prefer to be updated regularly, verbally, or with written memos. Be sure they know when to expect feedback about their performance. If there are times that they should not contact you, be sure that those times are clearly stated.

If you want to have a high level of control over all decisions, acknowledge that to all in the program. If you expect the doulas to have a high level of autonomy, be sure that you have been clear about that.

Determine what your priorities are and what you expect the doulas to be. The best managers focus people's efforts in order to avoid uncertainty. **The task of the doula program should be to serve and support the pregnant woman and her family.** This is true whether the doula program is an independent, private one or a hospital-based program. In a hospital-based program, there is a potential for the pregnant woman to feel that the doula is trying to please the hospital and not her. This happens because the woman feels that the hospital is the doula's primary client as they are a hospital employee. It is critical that the doula understand that even though she is an employee of the institution her main responsibility is to the pregnant woman and her family. This can be tricky and the politics of this type situation must be covered in either the doula training or on an individual basis with each doula.

For both private and hospital-based programs, it is advisable to set up one-on-one visits between a nurse, midwife, doctor or another doula who has worked with the doula to allow time for the discussion of the birth environment. This should be done as early as possible after the doula enters the program. These meetings should focus on the positives of the situations or problems that have occurred. It is also an opportunity to brainstorm together solutions to the problems and ways to prevent further problems. To get the most from this one-to-one meeting it should follow the following guidelines. *Set the meeting up in advance.* This allows all parties time to think about what issues they would like to discuss. *Have a goal for the meeting.* What do you want to achieve? *Choose the meeting location carefully.* The location should be a neutral one that is private to allow for the best communication. Eliminate any potential interruptions or distractions. *Agree on total honesty as a ground rule for the meeting. Both parties should use effective listening skills.* Try not to think of your reply while the other person is talking. Give compliments where they are deserved. If the information shared in this meeting is confidential, be sure that both parties understand this.

Tips for Managers of Doula Programs

Communicate to the doulas effectively that what they do affects not only the mother that they are caring for but the doula program.

Listen to what the clients and doulas are saying.

Involve the doulas in decisions, especially those that affect them directly.

Encourage networking so that the doula does not become isolated.

Obtain evaluations of each birth from the following people: the doula, the physician or midwife, and the nurses involved. Doing this lets all feel "in control" and proud that they are asked for their input

Develop ways for doulas to feel important by appointing them to task forces, committees or to research a project.

Review the doulas' performance at scheduled times throughout the year.

The reality is that the entire maternal healthcare team should operate as a service unit. In order to function as a service unit, all involved in caring for the pregnant woman and her family should ask the family the following questions.

What do we currently do that you want us to continue doing? What do we do that you would like us to stop altogether? What do we now do that you feel you should do for yourself?

With the answers to these questions, it is easier for everyone on the healthcare team to provide care at their level of expertise. Using this strategy provides everyone a voice in a dialogue. All people have the chance to provide information and their opinion. This promotes shared decision making and an increased chance for all to be feel good about the end result.   This avoids anyone feeling as if they are in an "I win-You lose" situation.

The responsibility for healthcare decisions should remain with the pregnant woman. After all, it is the responsibility of the client to make the appropriate decision for herself and her baby. This should be an integral part of the philosophy of nurses, physicians, childbirth educators, midwives, and professional labor assistants.

Promoting personal power within each person is what allows people to listen in a non-threatening atmosphere. It helps them to be able to listen effectively and is what moves them to action. This should be a part of every healthcare system.

When offering criticism always speak in sincere, non-threatening tones and stay focused on the outcome you are seeking. Focus on the facts as they are hard to argue with. Avoid saying "always," "never," "worst" and phrases such as "You don't," "You won't," and "You didn't." These turn into personal put-downs.

Working as Part of a Team
There are many objects of great value
which cannot be attained by unconnected
individuals, but must be attained if at all, by association.
Daniel Webster

Perhaps the greatest wisdom or asset as a doula is the ability to flexibly work within different "team" settings. This skill has been proven time and time again to be the cornerstone of a successful business setting. Above all, teamwork is paramount to the birth process in a hospital setting. No one can do it alone. Take for example, the fact that the mother works in connection with her body. Others then work in concert with her efforts toward a more empowering outcome.

A team is not simply a group of people. A group of people becomes a team as they work together to achieve a goal. Teams develop over time and tend to achieve more when they set their own goals and objectives. This is especially true when doulas work with nurses and doctors and all involved need to feel that they are valued. Perseverance is needed as it often takes time for true teamwork to develop. When a team is first working together, they will need to communicate very often so that they can learn to trust one another. When working in the healthcare system, one must learn to welcome diversity and focus on the strengths of each birth team member. Share information with each other many times and in as many ways as possible. Trust is built by building relationships. Do not forget to applaud the efforts of others while you, too, bring your best to the birth environment.

Most doula programs experience the following five specific stages of growth.

Searching

Individuals are a little confused about what they will do in this new program. They question all aspects of the program as everyone tries to answer the question, "What's in it for me?" This goes beyond the service nature most doulas feel and relates directly to their interactions with the rest of the medical team.

Defining

Doula program members are focusing on the task or actual objective to be completed. Many conflicts can occur in this stage as some individuals will be focusing on developing team fellowship and others on the task at hand. Everyone is asking "What do we need to achieve?" Conflicts arise when one individual wants to achieve the goal one way and another individual feels a different way is warranted.

Identifying

Program participants have set team goals and identify themselves as a team. The group of doulas has now become a team and has its own personality. Now all members are asking the question "How can we best achieve program goals?"

Processing

The team of doulas are working toward the defined goal. Individual team members freely exchange information to help one another contribute to the team. Feedback is freely given. There is less need for formal leadership and individuals are now asking "Who else will benefit from the information and how can we do this better?" As the doulas work together repeatedly with other healthcare personnel they will continue to improve on both their communication and team skills.

Disbanding/Reforming

When the doula has achieved the objective of helping a mother she will prepare for a new objective with another mother. At this point she is asking "What's next?"

Team Building

There are three types of teams and each has a distinctive format as indicated on the table below.

Team Type	Feature
Problem Resolution	Trust
Creative	Autonomy
Tactical	Clarity

In order for any of these types of teams to flourish, they must have structure that includes clear roles and accountability, an effective communication system, a system to monitor individual performance and provide feedback and fact based judgment. Each piece of this structure requires different things from team members. All team members should have clear roles and be accountable at all times. For team members to communicate effectively all information must be accessible to all members and must come from credible sources. There must be opportunities for each person to raise issues of concern that may not be on the agenda and there should be succinct methods for documenting issues raised and decisions made. Fact based judgments require assessment of motivation, attitude and perception.

Have those in your doula program or, if possible, the entire birth team regularly participate in team building exercises and activities. This can be done at regular meetings or special team building events. Team building exercises allow individuals to cognitively and physically re-examine their commitment to the importance of team work in the birth environment. One of the easiest team building exercises should be to identify and discuss individual value systems and how values combine to create an overall team values system. See the appendix for examples of these team building exercises.

It is especially helpful for large private doula programs or hospital-based programs to understand the elements of effective teams. All teams must have a clear elevating goal. High performance teams have both a clear understanding of the goal to be achieved and a belief that the goal embodies a worthwhile result. An ineffective team goal has become unfocused, not usually as a result of incompetence but because most problems are complex. Solving the problem may be even more complex and the degree of collaboration requires intense and constant concentration. A key factor in high and low function teams is the structure of the team itself. When there is a structural deficiency, it is typically identified as the most opportune time. In doula programs this could be during a labor and birth. For team success, it is imperative to select the right people for the right job. This is especially true for doula programs. The doulas must be matched to the objective at hand. A competent doula must have technical skills, critical thinking ability, personal competencies and good interpersonal skills. Unified commitment is often elusive but is very necessary for the success of the doula program. Program loyalty, spirit, and dedication are common characteristics of a successful doula program.   At the very minimum, there must always be effort on the part of each doula. Doula programs do not succeed without serious individual investment of time and energy. Commitment enhanced by involvement needs to be a straightforward and consistent theme of the doula program. Lack of unified commitment is often the largest downfall of an ineffective functioning doula program.   Working well together is a fundamental ingredient of a successful doula program and a fundamental part of that is trusting each other. The program must be based on honesty, openness, consistency and respect. This allows the program to stay focused on the needs of the mother and promotes more efficient communication and coordination. Trust improves the quality of collaborative outcomes and therefore a more satisfying birth experience for the mother. When all health team members trust each other, they are more apt to help each other as they are each involved and autonomous. Although a collaborative environment is often hard to achieve, it should be part of the goal at each birth.

Individual standards combine with team pressure to influence performance. The standards of all programs and organizations are determined by the extent to which they require themselves to meet objectives and honor the way they work together. It might be acceptable to deliver minimum levels of performance through questionable means while treating each other shabbily but all doula programs should find it unacceptable to do anything less than perform at the highest level of individual integrity while treating others in the program with the highest level of respect. External support and recognition are important and are usually noticed more for their absence than for their presence. Tangible support often lags behind philosophical support.

All doula programs must have a clear vision, must work toward creating a positive change in the maternity care system, and must unleash the talents of each individual doula. Doulas must have autonomy to achieve results. All involved must be willing to confront and resolve issues associated with inadequate performance and fairness must be a critical issue.

**The Eight Elements
of
Effective Doula Programs**

A Clear Elevating Goal
A Results Driven Structure
Competent Doulas
Unified Commitment
A Collaborative Environment
Standards of Excellence
External Support and Recognition
Principled Leadership

Chapter Twelve

Troubleshooting: The Voice of Experience

Loyalty

*Loyalty means not
that I agree with
everything you say or
I believe you are always
right. Loyalty means that
I share a common ideal
with you and that,
regardless of minor
differences, we fight for
it, shoulder to shoulder,
confident in one another's
good faith, trust,
constancy, and affection.*

Karl Menninger

Avoid being too willing to blame outside factors for the problems in your doula program. Eighty percent of all the obstacles to the success of your program will come from either within the program itself or those working with the program. Being clear about what is constraining the program is critical to dealing with it effectively. Exactly how you will diagnose your business problems will depend on the symptoms you are experiencing. You will experience many business crises and responding to them will be crucial to the success of your program. To come up with remedies to problems, make three lists with the following headings. What qualities of our program are most dysfunctional? What are our strongest attributes? What other traits does our program need? The answers to these questions will help you to build on your program's strengths, correct its weaknesses and develop other desirable qualities.

Realize that your program is having problems if doulas seem to unclear about the direction of the program; doulas compete with each other instead of cooperate; many hidden agendas and communication patterns are present; the tone of the program is negative; rigid thinking is present; and participants are locked into a "right way" of doing things.

When faced with a problem in your program, realize that your perception of the program affects your appraisal of the problem. Therefore it is important to gather your doulas together and brainstorm possible solutions. The seating in this meeting is important as every member of the team should carry equal weight; a horseshoe shaped seating pattern is best. Use newsprint to record the problem and possible solutions. You will find that some solutions are creative and some destructive. Don't worry about that during brainstorming; it will be dealt with later in the process. Take turns talking about possible solutions; always think about what you want to say before you say it by rehearsing it in your mind. If need be, ask others for more information about their solutions to assure thorough communication. You might find that several ideas are similar and they can be grouped or clustered together. Prioritize your possible solutions. You might need to take a break at some point in the meeting to work on a possible solution. Do not be afraid to ask the group for feedback on the possible solution proposed. This is where you will identify the destructive solutions that will yield conflict and tension as well as the creative ones that will yield purpose and a sense on integrity. To avoid working on too much at once, put some ideas in storage to be dealt with at a later date. At a later time, you can reconvene and deal with those stored solutions.

Clear effective communication along with documentation of any incidents that may occur is necessary in some instances. Revisiting and clarifying the mission statement of the doula program with those involved in the incident will also help. If you find that situations of this kind continue to occur, it is highly possible that the person involved in repeat incidents is either consciously or subconsciously trying to sabotage the program. Sabotage efforts come in many forms depending upon the perceived power of the saboturer. Research shows women tend to sabotage other women more frequently than men, and men sabotage less on both areas with women. Constantly reinforce that this program is a team effort and all people involved in the care of the laboring woman are valuable. When one woman benefits from a healthy, empowering birth experience, all birth team members benefit.

If you find that the market is saturated or your clients' needs have shifted, it is time for a change in your program. Many small business experts point to change as the foremost ingredient of a flourishing company. The change might entail a new product or service, an original twist on an old service or product or a service completely different from the existing business. The key to these changes is timing. One must learn to be a trend spotter. What is it that your potential clients are looking for now? Tune into their needs. Knowing when to make changes is often difficult. If these things are occurring in your program, a change might be indicated.

1.   You see other doula programs changing.
2.   Your clients are leaving you for other doula programs.
3.   You're more interested in something other that what you are doing.
4.   You dread doing this work.
5.   Your program is too big for you to handle.
6.   You have a great idea you can't stop thinking about.
7.   Your business is no longer supporting your lifestyle.
8.   You haven't learned anything new, talked to anybody new or tried anything new.

The Voice of Experience

As in everything in life, those that came before us can often provide us with the greatest insights. In the hopes that weeks, months, or even years can be taken off your learning curve, we offer the following advice from both hospital-based programs and independent businesses. The solutions to their challenges may help you to streamline your approach and make the path easier to endure as you embark on your journey of starting a doula program. While their challenges and answers may not parallel your exact situation, they can help to spark the creativity necessary to solve the complex issues that may arise. They may also help you to head off a problem before it even exists simply by having the knowledge that such a roadblock has occurred previously in a doula program.

Challenge:
Prevent problem from occurring upon starting a hospital-based doula program

Solution:
Much advance planning and discussion with medical and nursing staff. Present doulas in a non-threatening way by the program coordinators who were already staff nurses. Include potential problems in the training session for the doulas. Including all the nursing staff in the training session. Introduce the doula program as a pilot program.

Challenge:
Getting the hospital to buy into the concept of a doula program.

Solution:
Began by interfacing with upper management about the role and benefits of doulas and eventually procured a preceptor site for the program. This allowed the staff to get used to the doulas, see what they do, and get to know them better. This was done with no obligation on their part. This also helped our doulas gain certification faster.

Challenge:
Getting doulas to stay with our program as volunteers.

Solution:
Encouraged doulas to take hold of the "sow a good seed-reap a good harvest" principle. We also pay doulas a percentage of what the client is able to pay and encourage them to pursue private practice while they are working with our volunteer program.

Challenge:
Medical staff intimidated by the doula.

Solution:
Education, education, education... in-services for all staff and instructing all staff in the art of public relations and training doulas to preface a statement or question with "being that my role is non-medical and you are the medical professional, could you tell me, show me, allow me,,,etc." A little PR goes a long way. Also note the nurse's name and USE IT. Try bringing donuts, bagels, or other food for the staff. Food is a universal connector.

Challenge:
Meeting risk management's requirement for insurance.

Solution:
Sought an insurance agent that would go to bat for us. At the time there is no professional liability available for corporations (blanket policy). Took one year to procure insurance. When limits did not meet hospital requirements and the insurance company was not willing to write higher we went back into meetings with risk management. The situation was explained and we asked them what it would take for them to feel comfortable with the doulas working in the OB department. Additional items they required were a criminal background check and special wording in the contracts.

Challenge:
Acceptance of doula care by medical staff

Solution:
It helped to have the doula concept introduced by two nurses from the area with 15 years experience in the area.

Challenge:
How to decide what business I was really in. (e.g.: educator, birth doula, postpartum doula, sibling care, lactation consultation).

Solution:
Offered all the services up front and then tracked the demographics of what services the clients were requesting the most. Narrowed the focus by the three criteria 1). What the clients were requesting 2). What was easiest to market 3). What was the easiest to manage. In my case, postpartum doulas were in highest demand and the easiest to manage and market due to the focus placed on the high birth rate which was also an affluent area that could afford services.

Challenge:
Medical staff was waiting and calling the doula too late to come in for the woman's labor.

Solution:
Leave nothing to chance. Perhaps one person's perception of when the doula is needed is different from that of another medical professional's perception. Have a written guideline on when the doula should be notified. Arrive in this guideline procedure with the input of doctors, midwives, nurse, doulas and clients. Express the ability to avoid longer labors by starting comfort measures sooner. It may also help to have noted on the client's chart if they have a specific desire when they would prefer that they doula arrive. When asked, most families prefer the doula to come as soon as they themselves arrive at the hospital.

Challenge:
Providing accurate information to physicians and their office staff so referrals can be made frequently, confidentially and knowledgeably.

Solution:
Created a "Dining with Doula" event. Each month, a different physician's group is targeted and lunch is arranged on the day when the most number of physicians and staff are present. The same material may have to be presented several times to catch everyone, but it is still a very effective method. Average cost is $15.00/doula/month with the investment of one and one-half hours of time per event.

Challenge:
"Turf battle" between staff nurses and independent doula.

Solution:
Step back and look to see if we have any hidden agendas. Doula shows respect for the nurse, her experience, and medical expertise. Instead of letting misunderstandings build, deal with them immediately before they get passed on to other healthcare team members. Follow-up after the birth with a note of appreciation of the chance to resolve the difference.

Challenge:
Previous bad experiences with unprofessional doulas have left the professional doula to overcome the "bad reputation."

Solution:
Prior to the DONA certification and other certifying bodies and the subsequent grievance process, there was not a lot that could be done to set the "professional" and "unprofessional" doulas apart. Becoming a certified doula is something that can set you apart. Also try taking a 8 X 11 Sheet of paper and

reducing the DONA Standards of Practice and Code of Ethics down to 4 X 5 each, placing them side by side and copying so that both documents are on one side of the paper. On the other side, type a short resume which includes personal information, brief history of your training and experience, references and their phone numbers. At the bottom, you may want to include the certification and grievance process of your certifying body. Encourage those with whom you work to let you know whether you have overstepped the ethics or standards in any way. Asking for this document to be included in the client's permanent record is also extremely helpful in having all medical personnel see you as a professional.

Challenge:
Two doulas in partnership find that their personal lifestyles are creating a conflict in their friendship and professional life.

Solution:
Discussed their professional values and philosophy but decided to dissolve the partnership. One doula bought out the other's portion of the existing business and formed another sole proprietorship. Both doulas continue to take call for one another but they have separate businesses.

Challenge:
Hospital provides doulas, but individuals also bring in private/independent doulas. Although these doulas may not be in direct conflict with doctors and nurses, they have not always acted in accordance with hospital policies.

Solution:
Because the hospital can be liable for things that happen "within their walls," a hospital policy of what a doula can and cannot do should be devised and given to the private doula, so there is no misunderstanding.

Challenge:
More people would be interested in the services of a doula if they could get insurance coverage. How do we go about this?

Solution:
Keep submitting for payment for doula services. The more visibility these services have, the greater the chance of insurance companies re-visiting the benefit to them. Approach HMO's with the cost savings and benefits to their enrollees. Try the same with PPO's and other managed care plans. Lobby for the inclusion of doula services. Try getting a state bill passed that allows for elective licensure of the doulas for the purpose of obtaining third party reimbursement. See the appendix for a sample bill proposal.

Challenge:
A group of doulas that utilizes one primary doula and several backup doulas needs an effective way for the client to make contact with the correct person.

Solution:
Have a monthly calendar schedule with names, addresses, telephone numbers and pager numbers available to the client and all doulas. Make sure that the client receives the schedule for an adequate time on either side of her due date. This is also a great reference for last minute clients. See the appendix for a sample calendar.

Challenge:
How much does a back-up doula get paid if she does the birth and who does the postpartum visit- the primary doula or the back-up?

Solution:
The agreed upon deposit is given to the primary doula who completes the prenatal visit and interview and who also does the contract. If the back-up doula does the birth, she receives the balance at the postpartum visit. The doula that attends the birth does the postpartum visit to insure continuity of care.

Challenge:
A volunteer doula program has some volunteers that only work 10 hours/month. How will this volunteer doula help with a labor that exceeds that time frame?

Solution:
Know ahead of time which volunteers might be willing to extend this time frame. Have the volunteer check with the charge nurse to see if she can be placed with a woman who is further along in labor.

Challenge:
Some media coverage regarding birth and the involvement of a doula was negative and misleading, almost cynical in nature. Although this was an editorial, it was by a journalist at a major daily newspaper.

Solution:
The Doula Association responded with their own editorial, remaining tactful and professional in their response. A clarifying letter was also sent to the editorial writer who wrote the article, along with several pages of data to support birth facts and doula attended births. Several women also responded with complaints and feelings of being offended by the journalist's article, enough so, that the editorial writer published a retraction.

Challenge:
Our doulas leave the hospital alone, sometimes in the middle of the night, often in a dimly lit parking lot.

Solution:
Hospital security guards have arranged to walk a doula to her car whenever necessary or requested.

Challenge:
Getting respect from other members of the birth team.

Solution:
Of all the challenges, this is universal among all programs, private, independent, volunteer or hospital-based. Follow the advice you received regarding professionalism in this book and in all the resources you have read. Realize that doula programs are the wave of the future. Anything or anyone on the cutting edge, must endure the "test of time" and that is what the doula must do. Simply put, it will take time. Do not give up. Little by little you will earn trust and respect. By example, you can change the minds of the skeptics and as laboring women embrace the benefits a doula can provide, a necessity will be born from what is now for most, a luxury.

Challenge:
Difficulty in attracting a wide range of clients

Solution:
Our organization is best known for its homebirth practice and its natural childbirth classes. This is a plus, in terms of attracting doula clients whose desire is for an unmedicated hospital birth with few medical interventions. However, we have encountered difficulty in reaching more "mainstream" clients. They seem to have a fear that we will interfere with their desire for pain medication. We describe to them in very concrete ways that we can not only assist her with comfort measures but, if her desire is for medication or anesthesia, will alert the staff nurse of her wishes. This seems to reassure them that we will not criticize or otherwise interfere with their plans to have pain medication.

Challenge:
Unfriendly nurse

Solution:
Be respectful and phrase statements so that she understands it is the pregnant woman's wishes, not the doula's (example: Jill wishes to avoid an episiotomy, if possible.") Show the nurse that you are willing to get extra chux, hold the emesis basin, clean up amniotic fluid, etc. all these actions establish that you are of

assistance to the nurse as well as the mother. Writing a thank-you note after the birth to the nurse emphasizing your thanks for including you as a member of the birth team and how pleased you were with the medical care given the mother is also beneficial.

Challenge:
Working with a stillbirth

Solution:
Help the mother answer routine questions about her medical history. Discuss the options available regarding the birth/death. Have information readily available about funeral homes in the area, costs, and options regarding burial, cremation or release of the body to the hospital for disposal. If reluctance is voiced about seeing the baby, offer to see the baby and describe it to the mother first. While the mother and family is holding the baby, offer them the option of privacy. Do not rush them.

Challenge:
Unexpected cesarean section

Solution:
In this situation, it is easy for the mother to "get lost in the shuffle." If available, offer the mother the option of lowering the anesthesia screen so that she can see the baby lifted from here body. Assist the mother and partner in holding the infant as the nurses will be busy with other aspects of the surgery. Assist with photographs. Offer to stay with the mother if the partner wants to accompany the baby to the nursery or vice versa. Verbalize to the couple in front of the staff that disappointment is a normal emotion in this situation. If available, assist the mother with breastfeeding in the OR suite or recovery room.

Chapter Thirteen

Evaluating Your Program

Follow up to determine patient satisfaction is essential for the well being of either a private or hospital-based doula program. Most hospital-based programs are under intense scrutiny from other department heads and administration. Included in the appendix of this book is a sample follow-up survey for a doula program. Doula programs are often head liners in the numbers of satisfied customers. Quite frequently the program receives comments like the following from both staff and patients alike.

"I have never heard a laboring family say that they didn't need or appreciate a doula's continuous support."

"It is fantastic that we have more tools and techniques to help laboring women."

"I loved having someone with me constantly."

Consult the appendix for examples of patient evaluation forms. Ana Draa, a Houston based monitrice, has all her clients not only evaluate her services but those of the midwife/physician and the hospital. She then uses those evaluations with prospective new clients.

Doula Staff Evaluation

It will be necessary to review the doulas performance at regularly scheduled times throughout the year. These peer reviews are often standard for hospital-based doula programs as all hospital employees receive evaluations. If yours is a private program, it will be necessary to develop a review tool. Included in the appendix of this book is a sample of a doula program peer review tool as evaluations from those who work closest with the doula are often the most significant. Several peers would complete the form to assure fairness and offsets differing perspectives. After gathering the reviews, meet with the doula to discuss them. Doulas themselves should keep files of information that is relative to their review. These may include notes and letters from clients or professionals as well as attendance at continuing education offerings.

Receiving Feedback

Not everyone is comfortable with receiving feedback. When it comes to performance appraisals, most attention focuses on how managers give feedback but how employees receive feedback is equally important. Trainers Dennis and Dianne LaMountain suggest the following guidelines. You may want to distribute these to your doulas.

1. *Feedback is a gift.* Consider other's reactions to be a gift, requiring commitment and effort from the giver.
2. *Giving feedback is a risk.* So thank and reassure the giver.
3. *Perception is reality.* Accept the impact of your behavior as the other's reality. You don't have to agree with it.
4. *Distinguish impact and intent.* Focus on being curious about your impact, not defensive about your presumed intent.
5. *Look for the "germ of truth".* Adopt a "What can I learn from this?" attitude.
6. *Check for understanding.* Paraphrase to verify what you hear and clarify anything you are unsure about.
7. *Put the message in perspective.* The feedback relates to just one aspect of your behavior, not your worth as a person.
8. *Assume good intent.* Assume the giver values and wants to improve your relationship, even if the feedback expresses temporary dissatisfaction.
9. *Separate consideration from action.* Take time to think about what has been said before reacting.
10. *Be responsible for yourself.* Decide how much you can take, at what rate, and what you will do with the information.
11. *First impressions are valid.* Do not dismiss first impressions from new people because "they don't really know you yet". First impressions are important and they provide some useful data you wouldn't otherwise have.

Self-confidence is good but it is very helpful when evaluating your program to have someone around to let you know when you've got it wrong or need to change something. It is often hard to get honest feedback from people close to you. The following sources may be of help to you.

Your board of directors should have independent professionals on it who can help you. Your board of advisors are often your most helpful people. They are often business people as well as health professionals and can help you look objectively at your program. Be sure you have several people who, for a small compensation (such as lunch) will regularly give you an honest evaluation of your program, including the quality of the work, marketing efforts, client service, financials, etc. Ask those who have used your service how they view every part of the program. They have a unique perspective.

Outcomes Management

Outcomes management will probably be used if your doula program is hospital-based. Many certifying organizations such as Doulas of North America gather data as part of their certification process. Outcomes are identified and measured through data collection and analysis and are an important way of evaluating your doula program. Outcomes management uses information about outcomes to enhance clinical, quality and financial outcomes. The principles of outcomes management include questioning practices; recognizing that change is necessary ; accepting uncontrollable factors and valuing the outcomes management process. In actuality, it is not outcomes that are managed but the processes that drive the outcomes. Accurately processing the information gathered in data analysis one can accomplish outcome improvement. Use of outcomes management will not only help gather data regarding your program but help refine the care that is provided through the program as well as provide a better long term perspective about the program. This will help improve care given to mothers as well as improve the health of mothers and babies.

JCAHO Guide to Outcomes Assessment

1. Select a condition or procedure.
2. Assemble a collaborative practice team.
3. Define a purpose.
4. Narrow the scope.
5. Determine logistics of collecting data.
6. Identify instruments.
7. Ensure quality control of data.
8. Collect data.
9. Enter data into computer data base.
10. Analyze data.
11. Provide feedback and interpretation.
12. Connect the outcome to the process.

The Joint Commission For Accrediting Hospitals Organization (JCAHO) is an independent organization that accredits hospitals based on patient care within each department. The hospital must meet national standards in all its services. For example, in maternity care services areas that would be scrutinized would be things such a medical care, nursing care, patient education, adhering to policies and procedures, and compliance of the standards of the American Academy of Obstetrics and Pediatrics. It also focuses on an interdisciplinary approach that makes it necessary for each department to demonstrate the links they have with other departments within the hospital system that are necessary to provide comprehensive patient care. As a doula, one must be aware of the JCAHO status of the hospital where your are employed or are providing independent services for your client. Most generally, a JCAHO accreditation carries with it some prestige and guarantee of a certain level of care.

Your program is functioning well if all involved are working toward a common goal; cooperation is present even in the face of difference of opinion; everyone communicates openly and respectfully; all share pride in the accomplishments of others as well as the program itself; and flexibility is a key component. Having clients fill out a doula program follow-up survey is another way to get feedback about your program. A sample follow-up survey is included in the appendix of this book.

You will be faced with obstacles in your path as you start and run a doula program.   Remember the value that doulas provide so you will not limit the opportunities to position yourself as a resource in your community for both the short-term and long-term.   Doula care is important   not only to the physical outcome but to the emotional well being of both mother and baby.   Doula programs make a difference in how the mother perceives the birth experience. Her memories will affect not only how she views the experience but how she views herself as a woman, how she views herself as a mother, how she parents her child and how she handles any difficult task for the rest of her life.

The biggest obstacle is dealing with other agendas while managing to keep priorities straight and in the correct order. Continually do a reality check by requiring those that are involved in the program to continuously do self-examination.   Planning ahead, placing confirmation phone calls and communicating schedules to those affected are ways to try to overcome this obstacle.   To overcome hurdles in your path, remind yourself of the role of the doula- helping women make good decisions about their babies and their births while supporting them emotionally and physically during the process. Constantly keep in mind a doula is there to help clients identify needs, articulate goals and develop ways to make decisions.

Chapter Fourteen

Satisfaction and Success

*The return from your work must be the satisfaction which
that work brings you and the world's need for that work.
With that, life is heaven, or as near heaven as you can get.*
                                        W.E.B. DuBois

Your doula practice will be effective if it has forward thinking and direction, attention, flexibility and commitment, and if the program is based on planning ability, sound management practices, experience, technical support, focused goals and caring. If you reduce the number of personality conflicts between all of those involved in a doula program, it is easier to provide quality care to all childbearing women. No one cooperates with anyone who seems to be against them. All involved in the program should practice active listening with clients, colleagues, and health professionals.

Your doula program should leave a legacy of individualized care that promotes maternal self-esteem. Be ruthless in your commitment to honesty and in caring more about what is right than who is right. Welcome those who challenge your program as that is what helps you strive to provide high quality care.

Developing a Doula Program

Doula care in our present day maternity care system is a way of seeking out a new home for an idea that has been present for generations in many cultures. Doula programs are an innovative way of working to make life safer for mothers and babies. Doula programs are a way of responding to not only the needs of laboring mothers but of society. Doula programs are another way of telling the world that birth is a normal, natural life event and should be treated as such. Celebrate your doula program with an annual reunion for those for whom you have provided care. Invite all past clients and their babies to attend a simple but festive party. Not only will it be a good morale boost for the doulas but it is a wonderful way to help the mother remember how powerful and strong she was during her child's birth. The photos taken at the reunion can be used in an album for prospective clients to view. If you have taken the time to build a strong foundation in the community; have based your program on the normalcy of birth, the values of professional labor support to the woman, her infant, family and to society as a whole, it will support many years of success.

Nature is already as good as it can be.
It cannot be improved upon.
He who tries to redesign it, spoils it.
He who tries to redirect it, misleads it.
                                        Lao-tzu

Appendix

Statement of Purpose
The following statement of purpose was developed
by Sherri Urban, R.N.

The (name of your program) is a (state whether non profit or for profit) program for childbirth professionals and families concerned about positive birthing experiences. (Name of your program) believes that a birth is a healthful physical process, and an intense personal, spiritual, and emotional experience. A satisfying birth is vitally important to the development of a healthy family unit. Women and their families need special and skillful support and encouragement throughout the childbearing year, and particularly during labor and birth, to optimize the experience and outcome for all those involved in this dynamic process.

The demand for labor support is increasing as more couples recognize both the challenges inherent in experiencing a satisfying birth within the constraints of today's medicalized system, and the special skills labor assistants bring to the birthing process. Popular childbirth books and childbirth related organizations are both recommending that expectant parents seek the services of a professional labor assistant to provide continuous, caring encouragement and guidance to both the laboring woman and her partner.

We respect the freedom, self-determination, and ultimate personal responsibility of each individual. We are dedicated to the highest standards of moral, ethical, and professional conduct. We recognize both the intuitive abilities of professional labor assistants, and their responsibilities as professionals to continually update and improve their skills and knowledge. We encourage and support both the initial training and the continued growth of labor assistants through networking, study groups, seminars and membership in professional organizations.

(Name of your program) recognizes the work that needs to be done in improving the childbearing experiences of families today. We seek to facilitate awareness and communication among families, the medical community, and other childbirth professionals and organizations with regard to the contributions the professional labor assistant can make to a healthy birthing experience. A professional labor assistant has a special relationship with the birthing couple she serves. This relationship, by its nature personal and ongoing, should be the focus of studied interest as a means of achieving improved prenatal care, birth satisfaction, and postpartum adjustment for the new family unit.

Business Plan

Business Plan for a Doula Program

The table of contents for a business plan should include the following:
Executive summary
Introduction
Description of current situation
Details of the business and business trends
Cost effectiveness of the doula program
Results of research
Impact of a doula both emotionally and physically on the laboring mother
Your proposed program
Role of the doula including what she won't do as well as what she will do
How the doula program will be promoted
Physical needs of the program
Projected financial performance
Revenue for the program
Compensation or salaries
Marketing of the doula program
Doula program capital expenditures
Projected profit for the program
Bibliography
Time line for establishment of the doula program
Ethical considerations for the doula program including conduct,
        responsibilities to professional, client, colleagues and society
Standards of practice including scope of practice, continuity of care,
        training, apprenticeship or mentor program, and record keeping
Care Protocols
Procedures
Job Description for doulas and director of program which include:
        definition and purpose, policies, performance expectations,
        supervision, and documentation
Conflict Resolution

Executive Summary

The executive summary should detail the primary focus of the doula program. If this is a hospital-based program, it should include information on the focus of the program within the existing hospital maternity service. If this is a private program, it should include information on the focus of the program within the community.

Following are samples of the type of information that should be included regarding focus of a hospital-based program.

Develop a competitive program which would differentiate (Name of Hospital) from other maternity services
The ability to increase patient numbers and at the same time reduce maternity costs
Promote the image of (Hospital Name) as a clinical center of excellence in providing family centered maternity care
The unique opportunity to model a comprehensive program in an integrated plan hospital system

Following are samples of the type of information that should be included regarding focus of a private program.

Develop a program which would differentiate this program from other types of maternity services.
The ability to improve the quality of maternity care while decreasing the costs of the same
The unique opportunity to model client-focused, individualized, maternity care with continuous care during labor and birth

Comments should also be included here about the goal of the program. Following is a sample of the goals for both a private and hospital-based program:

The goal of this private doula program is to develop a comprehensive doula program that meets the emotional and physical needs of the laboring mother and her partner. This program will help lower cesarean rates, decrease medical interventions, and reduce the need for epidural anesthesia.

The goal of this hospital-based doula program is to develop a comprehensive doula program that is congruent with the overall philosophy of maternity services and meets the needs of patients, families, staff and physicians. This program will help assure that (Name of Hospital) remains on the leading edge in maternity care.

Details of the planning process should be included:
For a hospital-based program this should provide information on:
      Evaluation of the hospital's current maternity services
      Identification of industry trends
      Analysis of the hospital competition
      Identification of marketing opportunities
      Financial projection
For a private program this should provide information on:
      Evaluation of the maternity services currently available in the community
      Identification of industry trends
      Analysis of any competing doula programs
      Identification of marketing strategy
      Financial projection

Introduction

The introduction should give general information about birth, its psychological and sociological ramifications and how the doula will enhance those processes. It should detail information that relates how the work of the doula will affect the life of the woman as well as detail how the role of the doula is one of nurturing and protection of a woman's memory of the birth experience.

It should also discuss how doula programs are beginning to be recognized as an integral component of family centered maternity care and projections for the future.

Information should be included here on the market survey indicating that the community is in need of a doula program and why.

The Industry
Description of the Business and Trends

Information such as that below is the type that should be included in the description of the business and trends.

Women continue to look at birthing a healthy baby as their #1 priority but are also looking to have a more positive experience in terms of emotional and psychological satisfaction.   Doula support programs in a hospital setting are comparatively new and are being implemented to answer the requests of women's desire for continuity of care, providing an advocate inside the hospital system as well as a means of reducing obstetrical costs and increasing patient numbers.   Private doula support programs have been in place since the early 1980's as shown detailed in the research for *Special Women: The Role of the Professional Labor Assistant*, the first book about doulas and monitrices.

Eleven scientific studies, which were conducted for various lengths of time, in various settings, show marked reductions in cesarean sections, epidurals, narcotic use, oxytocin use, length of labor, forceps use, and postpartum depression.   Other increases seen are   improved breastfeeding, heightened self-esteem of the mother, and mother/infant bonding.

In the clinical arena of staff shift changes, managed care, and on-call physicians, the doula may be the only person to provide continuous care from the prenatal period to the postpartum home visit.   In the past twenty years, doulas have been working as independent providers of emotional and physical support to women in labor.   As families, physicians and hospitals saw the positive results directly related to the presence of the doula, their services were welcomed to the point of physicians making requests for their patients to be attended by a doula.

Several professional organizations (Association for Labor Assistants and Childbirth Educators (ALACE), Childbirth Education Foundation (CEF) and Doulas of North America (DONA) have been formed and individuals such as Paulina Perez, Cheri Grant, Penny Simkin, Cindy Kerbs, and Kathy Bradley are also providing doula education and training.

There are now hospitals across the country providing doula programs as an "in-house" service. They are looking to better meet the needs of the pregnant patients and at the same time be able to reduce costs. In an era of shortened hospitals stays and the need to continue providing quality care, the doula is proving to be a vital asset.

In the next few years we will see both more hospitals providing doula services and more private programs as well as insurance companies working hand-in-hand with these programs to include this coverage.

Cost Effectiveness of Doula Attended Births

According to data available to day,

Of every 100 women having a baby,
50 will have epidural anesthesia @ $1,000,000 = $50,000,000
25 will have a cesarean section @ $7,000,000 = $175,000,000
75 will have a vaginal birth @ $3,000,000 = $225,000,000

Total Cost of 100 births   **= $450,000,000**

According to **conservative** estimates of the doula's value,

Of every 100 women having a baby with a doula,
30 will have an epidural anesthesia @ $1,000,000 = $30,000,000
20 will have a cesarean section @ $7,000,000   = $140,000,000
80 will have a vaginal birth @ $3,000,000 = $240,000,000
Add the cost of a doula @ $300 = $30,000,000

Total Cost of doula attended births = $440,000,000

Total Cost Savings per 100 births with doulas = $10,000,000

Approximately 4,000,000 births take place each year in the USA. If only 1 woman in 4 has a doula attend her birth, the costs savings would be $10 million a year.

These figures are based on the research of Klaus, Klaus, & Kennell

Combined Results of 6 Randomized Controlled Trials on Labor Support

Obstetrical Outcomes

Outcome	Doula Effect
Length of labor	25% decrease
Oxytocin use	40% decrease
Narcotic use	30% decrease
forceps use	30% decrease
epidural use	60% decrease
cesarean section	50% decrease

Other findings
decrease in maternal fever
decrease in infant days in NICU
decrease in infant septic workups
Long Term Benefits
Improved breastfeeding
Increased time spent with infant
More positive maternal assessments of infant's personality, competence, and health
Decreased postpartum depression

Information from the work of Klaus, Klaus, & Kennell

The Impact of a Doula on Labor and Early Parenting

Support in labor by a doula produces:

> Increased positive feelings about labor (2, 4)
> Decreased need for medication (1,3, 4)
> Decreased intervention (3)
> Decreased cesarean sections (3)
> Decreased anxiety (3, 4)
> Decreased tension (3)
> Shortened labor (3)
> Increased acceptance of the baby (2)
> Enhancement of maternal/infant bonding (2,3)
> *Decreased neonatal problems (3)
> Increased maternal self-esteem (1,2, 4)
> *Increased maternal cooperation
> *Decreased postpartum depression

When the laboring woman's emotional needs are met, clinical outcomes are improved for both mother and baby (1,2,3). In addition, the long term impact may be enhanced self-confidence and self-esteem in the mother (4).

*These areas are of special concern in relationship to positive birth experiences for all concerned and in the area of reducing cost and providing cost savings.

References:
1.   Hodnett, Ellen D. And Osborn, Richard. "A randomized trial of the effects of monitrice support during labor: Mothers Views of Two to Four Weeks Postpartum." *Birth,* 16:4, December 1989.
2.   Hofmyer, G.J. et al. "Companionship to modify the clinical birth environment: Effects on progress and perceptions of labor and breastfeeding," *British Journal of Obstetrics and Gynaecology,* 98:756-764, 1991.
3.   ` Kennell, J., et al. "Continuous emotional support during labor in a US hospital." *Journal of the American Medical Association,* 265:2197-2201, May 1, 1990.
4.   Perez, Paulina and Snedeker, Cheryl. *Special Women: The Role of the Professional Labor Assistant*, Cutting Edge Press, 1994.

Private Monitrice Practice
Polly Perez, 1980-1996

The following data is from a private labor support practice in Houston, Texas of both low and high risk clientele. The clientele for this practice included women with a uncomplicated pregnancy as well as those with a diagnosis of gestational diabetes mellitus, pregnancy induced hypertension, multiple pregnancy,

pregnancy complicated by vaginal bleeding, breech presentation and uterine fibroids. You will note that a large section of the births reported are from women with a previous cesarean section delivery. The deliveries were conducted in tertiary care hospitals (level III), community hospitals (level II), freestanding birth centers and at home.   Primary care givers included obstetricians, perinatologists, and certified nurse midwives.

Clients	649
Vaginal Births	572
Cesarean Sections	77 (11.8%)

Vaginal Birth After Cesarean

VBAC Attempts	155
VBAC Vaginal Births	132 (85.2%)
Cesarean after VBAC attempt	23 (14.8%)

Previous Cesareans	VBAC Attempts	Vaginal Births	C/Sec
1	125	113(90%)	17
2	27	19(70%)	7
3	1	1	0

Doula Support Service
Proposed Program

Role of the Doula

The doula is a provider of non-medical, physical and emotional support to the laboring woman and her partner. The doula meets with a woman prenatally, assists at the labor and birth, and continues to support her with a postpartum home visit.

The doula role is separate from that of the nurse. The doula offers no clinical skills and does not perform any medical tasks. Her sole function is to give emotional and physical support, suggest comfort measures and facilitate communication between the woman, her partner, and other medical personnel.

The doula does not replace the woman's partner or other people she has chosen to help her. Partners have found the presence of a doula to be very helpful as it takes the pressure off them. The doula's availability allows the partner to relax and share in the emotional experience of the birth.

Promoting the Doula Program to Others

(Name of Hospital or Private Program) will be the first in the area and one of the few across the nation. As the need for doulas is recognized, (Name of Hospital or Private Business) will easily be able to market its program. It is projected that doula programs will become an integral part of maternity care and those that have a program already in place will be in great demand for advice and guidance.

There is no doubt that there will be a program package to market. This will provide a source of revenue to the hospital or business in addition to the savings that will be seen by hospitals as a result of increased patient numbers and decreased medical costs. Being able to promote and sell this program will be one more reason why (Name of hospital or business) will be a community leader in providing family centered maternity care.

Physical Needs for Doula Program

The following items are needed to accommodate the doula program which will begin initially with (#) doulas and a coordinator who also works as a doula.

* Office Space	* Desk and chair	*Side chair
* File cabinet	* Computer	*Phone and answering machine

* Pagers   * Uniforms   (scrub pants and shirt or tee shirt)

* Texts for doulas to include the following: *Special Women: The Role of the Professional Labor Assistant. The Nurturing Touch at Birth: A Labor Support Handbook, Mothering the Mother,* and *Labor Support Forms: A Guide for Doula Charting,*
* Birth bags to include the following: Gymnastik labor/birth ball, hot/cold comfort wrap, Happy Massager, Birth Ball cover, Labor Support Reminder Cards, ice wrap, two mini massagers, foot cream and body lotion for massage.

Hospital Program Expenses
Salaries

1.0 FTE Doula Program Coordinator (Salaried position)	$28,800.00
(#) Doulas volume # of births X $300	To be determined by
Consultant charges (includes training of initial group of doulas and doula trainer)	$6,000
Certification fees	To be determined by # of doulas
Continuing education	$3,000.00
Total Salaries salaries	$38,400.00 + doula

Marketing
Brochures and written materials	$2,500.00
Advertising includes newspaper and bill boards	$10,000.000
Speaker for community presentation	$1500.00
Food and beverage	$500.00
Total Marketing	$14,500.00

Capital expenditures
File cabinet	$500.00
Desk	$450.00
Computer	$2,500.00

Pagers $2,000.00
Phone and answering machine $50.00
Uniforms   Cost to be determined by # of
                                              doulas

Birthing bags
(#)@ $185.00   Cost to be determined by # of
                                              doulas

Doula books
(#) sets @ $70.00   Cost to be determined by # of
                                              doulas

Total Capital Expenditures   Total

Reading List and Bibliography for Doulas

Ament, Lynette et al., "Sexually Transmitted Diseases in Pregnancy: Diagnosis, Impact and Intervention," *JOGNN* 25:8, October 1996.

Bennett, A., et al. "Antenatal preparation and labor support in relation to birth outcomes, " *Birth* 12(1):9-15, Spring 1985.

Burda, D., "Providers Look to Industry for Quality Models," *Modern Healthcare* 18(29):24-26,28,30-32.

Cranley, MS, et al. "Women's perceptions of vaginal and cesarean deliveries," *Nurs Res* 32(1):10-15, Jan/Feb 1983.

Hemminki E, Virta A-L, Koponen P, Malin M, Koho-Austin H, Tuimala R. "A trial on continuous human support during labor: feasibility, interventions and mothers' satisfaction," *J Psychosom Obstet Gynaecol* II:239-250, 1990.

Highley BL, et al. "Safeguarding the laboring woman's sense of control," *Am J of Maternal Child Health.* 3(1):39-41, Jan/Feb 1978.

Hodnett ED, et al. "A randomized trial of the effects of monitrice support during labor: mothers' views two to four weeks postpartum," *Birth* 16(4):177-183, Dec 1989.

Hodnett ED, Osborn RW. "Effects of continuous intrapartum professional support on childbirth outcomes," *Research in Nursing and Health.* 12(5):289-297, 1989.

Hofmyr GJ, Nikodem VC,Wolman WL, Chalmers BE, Kramer T. "Companionship to modify the clinical birth environment: effects on progress and perceptions of labour and breastfeeding," *Br J OB/Gynaecology* 98:756-764, 1991.

Keirse MJNC, Enkin M, Lumley J. "Social and professional support during childbirth," *Effective Care in Pregnancy and Childbirth*, Vol 2, Chalmers I, Enkin M, Keirse MJNCm eds. NY:Oxford University Press, 1989.

Kennell J, Klaus M, McGrath S, Robertson S, Hinkley C. "Continuous emotional support in labor in a US hospital: A randomized controlled trial," *JAMA* 265(17): 2197-2237, May 1, 1991.

Klaus M, Kennell J, Berkowitz G, Klaus P. "Maternal assistance and support in labor: Father, nurse, midwife, or doula?" *Clinical Consultations in Obstetrics and Gynecology*, 4(4):211-217, December 1992.

Klaus MH, Kennell JH, Robertson SS, Sosa R. "Effects of social support during parturition on maternal and infant morbidity," *Br Med J.* 293(6547):585-7, 1986.

Klaus, Klaus and Kennell. *Mothering the Mother*, Addison Wesley.

McNiven P, Hodnett E, O'Brien-Pallas LL. "Supporting women in labour: a work sampling study of the activities of intrapartum nurses," *Birth.* 19(1):3-8, 1992.

Perez, Paulina. "Another Kind of Labor Partner," *Lamaze Parents Magazine*, Doubleday, N.Y., 1997.

Perez, Paulina, "Childbirth Educators as Doulas: Helping Improve Perinatal Outcomes," *Genesis*, October 1994.

Perez, Paulina, "Reclaiming the Birth Experience, Women and Newborn Health," *Washington University Perinatal Center*, 10:2, Spring 1997.

Perez, Paulina. "Reflections of a Monitrice," *Childbirth Forum*, Spring 1995.

Perez, Paulina and Snedeker, Cheryl, *Special Women: The Role of The Professional Labor Assistant*, Cutting Edge Press, Katy, Texas, 1994.

Perez, Paulina. "The Doula & Active Management of Labor," *The International Doula*, 4:2, Summer 1996.

Perez, Paulina, *The Nurturing Touch at Birth: A Labor Support Handbook*, Cutting Edge Press, Katy, TX, 1997.

Radin, TG, et al., "Nurses' care during labor: its effect on the cesarean birth rate of healthy, nulliparous women," *Birth*. 20(1):14-21, Mar 1993.

Richardson, P., "Approach and avoidance behaviors by women in labor toward others," *Mat Child Nurs J.* 8(1):1-21, Spring 1979.

Rosen, MG, "Doula at the bedside of the patient in labor," *JAMA*. 265(17):2236-2237, 1 May 1991.

Shearer, B. "Doula at the bedside of the patient in labor," *Childbirth Educator*. Spring:26-31, 1989.

Simkin, P. "The labor support person: Latest addition to the maternity care team," *ICEA Review*, 16(1):19-27, Feb 1992.

Smith, AA, "A critical review of labor and birth care," *J Family Practice* 33(3):281-292, 1991.

Sosa R, Kennell J, Klaus M, Robertson S, Urrutia J., "The effect of a supportive companion on perinatal problems, length of labor, and mother-infant interaction," *New Eng J Med* 303(11):597-600, 1980.

Thornton JG, Lilford RJ. "Active management of labour: current knowledge and research issues," *Br Med J* 309:366-369, 6 Aug 1994.

Wolman WL, Chalmers B, Hofmyr GH, Nikodem V. "Postpartum depression and companionship in the clinical birth environment: A randomized controlled trial," *Am J OB & Gynecology,* 168(5):1388-1393, May 1993.

Zhang, J, et al., "Continuous Labor support from labor attendant for primiparous women: A meta-analysis," *Obstetrics & Gynecology*, 88(4):Part 2, 739-744, October 1996.

Proposal for a Volunteer Labour Support Program in a Canadian Hospital
Used with permission

This proposal outlines a program of volunteer labour support provided to laboring women at a Canadian hospital.   Labor Support services would be provided "on-call" and free of charge to women and their partners, and would be administered through the hospital auxiliary.   A telephone number contacting a member of the doula program would be contacted upon admission to the hospital and a doula would be sent to support the requesting woman. The doulas participating in this program would meet the prerequisites and qualifications of the Community Birth Care and the hospital.   Benefits to the hospital included reduced medical costs, reduced lengths of labour and constant supervision of labours.   Benefits to the laboring women and their partners include shorter labours, increased satisfaction with the birth experience and increased bonding of newborn and parents.   The program would also provide trained doulas the opportunity to acquire valuable experience in their profession and to promote the local acceptance of labour assistance as a profession.

What is Community Birth Care?

Community Birth Care is a recently formed group of doulas comprised of professional, supportive and knowledgeable women. We represent many fields of experience, including education, massage therapy, embryo transfer, reflexology and homeopathy who and have acquired further special training through the International Childbirth Education Association, Doulas of North America and La Leche League International.   We have all completed the Conestoga College course "Principles of Labour Support."   Labour Support providers must be actively seeking certification by Doulas of North America in order to qualify for membership in Community Birth Care.   This includes abiding by DONA's Code of Ethics and Standards of Practice.

What is a doula and what does she do?

A doula is a Greek word referring to an experienced woman who helps other women.   The word has now come to mean a woman experienced in childbirth who   provides continuous physical, emotional and informational support to the mother before, during and just after childbirth.

-Klaus, Klaus & Kennell. *Mothering the Mother*

A doula...

- recognizes birth as a key life experience, understands the physiology of birth and the emotional needs of a woman in labour
- assists the woman and her partner in preparing for and carrying out her plans for the birth
- stays by the side of the labouring woman throughout the labour with no change in shift
- provides emotional support, practical comfort measures, an objective viewpoint and information to aid in decision-making

- facilitates communication between the labouring woman, her partner and clinical care providers
- complements the care provided by the woman's partner and other birth attendants

Benefits of Labour Support to the Mother

- increases positive feelings about labour (2)
- decreases intervention (3,5)
- decreases need for medication (1,3,5)
- decreases cesareans (3,5)
- increases acceptance of the baby (2,5)
- enhances maternal/infant bonding (2,3,5)
- decreases neonatal complications (3,5)
- decreases anxiety and tension (3.5)
- shortens labour (3.5)
- increases other's feelings of self-esteem (1.2)
- increases feelings of control (1.2)
- increases mother's cooperation and participation (6)
- decreases postpartum depression (6)

1. Hodnett and Osborn, " A randomized trial of the effects of monitrice support during labor," *Birth* 16:4, December 1989.
2. Hofmyr et al. "Companionship to modify the clinical environment: Effects on progress and perceptions of labor and breastfeeding." *Br J OBGYN* 98:1991.
3. Kennell, Klaus et al. "Continuous emotional support during labor in a US hospital," *JAMA*, 265:May 1, 1990.
4. Simkin, P. "Just another day in a woman's life?" *Birth* 18:4, 1991.
5. Sosa, Klaus and Kennell. "The effects of a supportive companion on perinatal problems, length of labor and mother-infant interaction," *NEngJM* 303:1980.
6. Wolman, et al. "Postpartum depression and companionship in the clinical birth environment" *AMJ OBGYN*. May 1993.

The following chart is a summary of 6 randomized, controlled trials on labor support.

Obstetrical Outcomes	Doula Effect
Cesarean Section	50% decrease
Length of Labour	25% decrease
Oxytocin Use	40% decrease
Pain medication se (narcotics)	30% decrease
Forceps	60% decrease
Epidural Use	60% decrease

Long term benefits

Improved breastfeeding
Increase time spent with baby
More positive maternal assessment of baby's
        personality, competence and health
Decreased postpartum depression

Other findings

decrease in maternal fever
decrease in NICU admissions
decrease in sepsis workups

Benefits of the program to labour support providers
Beyond the personal satisfaction associated with providing labour support, doulas in the Waterloo-Wellington area would benefit by increased experience in their field, meeting qualifications for certification by DONA and promoting the recognition and acceptance of birth labour assistance as a profession.

Structure of the Proposed Program
        A telephone number would be posted at the main desk of the maternity wing. Appended to the list would be documents explaining the role of the doula and the advantages of labour support.   The phone number would provide contact with a member of Community Birth Care and that member would be responsible for finding a doula to fill the request for labour support. All doulas participating in the program would meet the requirements for membership in Community Birth Care as well as the hospital auxiliary program. As each labouring woman was admitted to the hospital, she would be advised that labour support could be made available to her and at no charge. The woman or her partner would be free to call the CBC number at their discretion. No
effort from hospital staff would be required. The doula would remain at the women's side throughout the duration of the labour and delivery. The following services would be provided at that time.
- support for the woman's primary partner
- relaxation techniques
- positioning techniques
- labour coping skills
- comfort measures for birth and immediate postpartum
- working with a long of difficult labour
- VBAC support
- breastfeeding support, if requested

Summary
        It is the goal of Community Birth Care to provide labour support services to pregnant women upon admission to the hospital on a "pro bono" basis. A volunteer would be admitted into the labour room as a "support provider" and under the auspices of the hospital auxiliary. The advantages of labour support have been thoroughly documented in this proposal and include reduced medical

costs, reduced lengths of labour, increased satisfaction with the birth experience and increased bonding with the infant.

We believe that the implementation of a volunteer program as described above, will enhance the birth experience of the women, provide a useful volunteer service to the hospital, and promote recognition and acceptance of the labour support profession in this area.

(Name of your Business)
Balance Sheet

Assets	1997	1998

Current Assets
Cash
Accounts receivable
Inventory
Prepaid Expenses
   Total Current Assets

Property and Equipment
Net of depreciation
Other Assets, Deposits
   Total Assets

   Liabilities & Current Equity
Current Liabilities
Note Payable, Line of credit
Accounts Payable
Current Long-Term Debt
Withheld and Accrued payroll Taxes
Income Taxes Payable
   Total Current Liabilities
Long-Term Liabilities
Loan Payable
Note Payable
Total Long-Term Liabilities
Total Liabilities

Owners' Equity
Common Stock Issued
Additional Paid-In Capital
Retained Earnings
   Total Owners' Equity
   Total Liabilities & Owners' Equity

1997	1998
Net Revenues	Net Revenues
Net Income	Net Income

LABOR SUPPORT INCOME

DATE	CLIENT	INV. #	DEPOSIT	BALANCE	TOTAL FEE	TIP/GIFT	DONA-TION	VOLUN-TEER	HOURS	EXPENSE	INCOME

SAMPLE

Adapted with permission from Barbara Ross-Ellis, *From Start to Finish: A Practical Guide to Your Labor Support Business* (1991)

LABOR SUPPORT EXPENSE

DATE	EXPENSE	TRAVEL	OFFICE	PHONE	GIFT	FILM	CHILD CARE	SUPPLIES	EDUCAT.	BANK	ADVER.	POSTAGE	PUBLI-CATIONS	MISC.
		GAS MILEAGE PARKING	SUPPLIES COPYING STATIONERY	MONTHLY LG. DIST. MOBILE PAGER		PROCESSING FILM CAMERA VIDEOS		BOOKS CLD BIRTH MATERIALS LABOR BAG VIDEOS	CONFER. PLANE FARE HOTEL FOOD	FEES	Y. PAGE BROCHURE NEWSPAPER BUS. CARDS	STAMPS	DUES DONA LOCAL	

SAMPLE

Adapted with permission from Barbara Ross-Ellis, *From Start to Finish: A Practical Guide to Your Labor Support Business* (1991)

Anatomy and Physiology of Pregnancy for the Doula and Monitrice
Basic Questions

1. Name the 4 basic pelvic types.

2. Name the supporting ligaments of the uterus.

3. Name the 4 types of breech presentations.

4. Identify 8 vertex presentations.

5. Descent into the pelvis is measured according to the relationship between the presenting part and_____.

6. Name the two sides of the placenta and tell what each looks like.

7. What is one of the most effective positions for helping a posterior baby to rotate?

8. Name three signs of true labor contractions.

9. What 6 things should you check for when doing a vaginal exam?

10. The average duration of pregnancy is _____days.

11. What are the cardinal movements in the mechanism of labor?

12. Name the three phases of the first stage of labor and define them.

Common Medical Abbreviations

AB	abortion	GDM	gestational diabetes mellitus
abd	abdomen		
ac	before meals	gtts	drops
adlib	as needed	GTT	glucose tolerance test
		HELLP	hemolysis of red blood cells elevated liver enzymes, low platelets
AFP	alpha fetoprotein		
amb	ambulate		
AROM	artificial rupture of membranes		
BID	twice a day	Hx	history
BM	bowel movement	IAB	induced abortion
BOW	bag of waters	IM	intramuscular
BP	blood pressure	IUGR	intrauterine growth retardation
BPD	bi-parietal diameter		
BSST	breast stimulation stress test	IUP	intrauterine pregnancy
		L&D	labor and delivery
c	with	LGA	large for gestational age
CAN	cord around neck	LLQ	left lower quadrant
CBC	complete blood count	L/min	liters per minute
cc	cubic centimeters	LML	left meiolateral
cm	centimeters	LMP	last menstrual period
c/o	complains of	L/S ratio	lecithin-sphingomylein ratio
contx	contraction		
CPD	cephalopelvic disproportion	mec	meconium
		ml	milliliters
CVS	chorionic villi sampling	mmHg	millimeters of mercury
cx	cervix	neg	negative
DC	discontinue	NPO	nothing by mouth
D&C	dilatation and curettage	NA	not applicable
D&E	dilatation and evacuation	nl	normal
decel	deceleration	NR	non reactive
DIC	disseminated intravascular coagulation	NST	non-stress test
		NSVD	normal spontaneous vaginal delivery
DIU	death in utero		
DTR	deep tendon reflex	OCT	oxytocin challenge test
EBL	estimated blood loss	PE	physical exam
EDC	expected date of confinement	PID	pelvic inflammatory disease
EDD	expected date of delivery	PIH	pregnancy induce hypertension
EFW	estimated fetal weight		
FHR	fetal heart rate	PKU	phenlyketonuria
FHT	fetal heart tone	pc	after meals
FTT	failure to thrive	po	by mouth
		prn	when needed

pt	patient
q	every
qd	every day
qh	every hour
QID	four times a day
QOD	every other day
RDS	respiratory distress syndrome
r/o	rule out
Rx	prescription
s	without
SAB	spontaneous abortion
SGA	small for gestational age
SOB	short of breath
SROM	spontaneous rupture of membranes
stat	immediately
SVD	spontaneous vaginal delivery
TID	three times a day
TORCH	toxoplamosis, other, rubella, cytomegalovirus and herpes
TTP	transient tachypnea
tx	treatment
UA	urinalysis
US	ultrasound
UTI	urinary tract infection
WNL	within normal limits

Doula Self Knowledge Questions

Every doula should ask herself these basic questions after obtaining training and before starting work as a doula.

1. What is the potential psychological impact of the birth experience on the life of a woman?
2. What is my role as a labor support person or "doula"?
3. Describe cervical effacement and dilatation.
4. What is oxytocin? Pitocin?
5. Why is relaxation important during labor?
6. During labor, what might I say to a woman that will provide verbal encouragement?
7. What five or six positions would provide comfort for and/or encourage labor progress?
8. Define contraction interval and contract time.
9. Can I define EFM (electronic fetal monitoring) and its pros and cons?
10. What type of drugs are available for use for pain relief during labor? What are their pros and cons?
11. What are some of the common reasons for cesarean sections? Define each.
12. What techniques can the doula suggest to help relieve "back labor?"
13. What are the benefits during labor to each of the following positions: ambulating, hands & knees, side lying, squatting, rocking, or swaying?
14. How will I communicate with the "birth team" (physicians, midwives, nurses) most effectively?
15. What support measures can I offer the woman's partner or family?
16. List five different labor support tools that the doula can use.
17. Why is postpartum followup with the mother so important?
18. How can I enhance the relationship between the mother and the medical staff?.
19. What should I discuss with the family after the birth to ensure a good birth memory for them?
20. List three symptoms of postpartum depression.
21. Can I explain how postpartum depression and post traumatic stress differ?
22. When might I use the following techniques: the dangle, stomp-squat, abdominal lift?
23. How will I respond to the question; "Why should I have a doula?" when asked about the work I do?
24. What are the benefits to intracutaneous injections of sterile water for backache during labor?

Agreement for Private Doula Service

Following is another type of contract developed by Ana Draa, a labor assistant with a Houston, Texas based private practice. It contains the essential components of all contracts (a heading, introductory statement, commitments, restrictions or conditions and signatures).

The following sets forth an agreement between Doula (**Name**), Client (**Name**) and Client's Partner (**Name**).

I.   **Services the Doula Agrees to Provide:**
        Doula accompanies Client in labor to help achieve a satisfying birth experience and help Client give birth in the manner Client desires. Doula received education for the Doula's role from attending workshops & apprenticing with several local monitrices. Doula draws on her knowledge and experience to provide emotional support and physical comfort. Doula assists Client in gaining the information needed to make informed decisions throughout her birth. Doula is self-employed and does not work for a hospital, birth site or other healthcare professional.
        Doula would prefer to meet with Client & Client's partner at least once before labor. During this meeting, Doula, Client and Client's Partner will complete a Prenatal Questionnaire in order to understand Client's priorities, Client's own best ways of coping with pain and fatigue, Client's preferences regarding management options and the use of pain medications and to discuss any other concerns. Additionally during this meeting, Doula. Client and Client's partner will discuss how they might best work together. Doula will also assist Client in preparation for a birth plan, if requested.
        Doula will inform Client of times when Doula is unavailable for labor support. To cover those times, Doula has agreements with back-up Doulas and will make every reasonable effort to have a back-up Doula attend the birth.
        Doula agrees to meet Client in labor within two hours after receiving a call from Client requesting her presence. Doula will remain with Client throughout Client's labor and birth, providing comfort measures, reassurance and doing everything reasonably possible (except as noted in Paragraph II) to help Client achieve her birth desires. Doula can help initiate breastfeeding, if requested. Doula will remain with Client for up to two hours after the birth unless Client is comfortable and ready for Doula to leave earlier. After the birth, Doula will be available for phone contact to answer questions. Doula would like to get together with Client within two weeks after the birth to see how Client is doing, to review the birth and to get feedback from Client about Doula's role.

II.   **Services NOT Provided by the Doula:**
        Doula will not make decisions for Client. Doula will help Client get the information necessary to make informed decisions. Doula will not speak to

Hospital Staff (i.e. doctors, midwives, nurses, any hospital employee) on Client's behalf. Doula will discuss Client's concerns with Client and suggest options, but the Client or Client's partner will be responsible for speaking to the Hospital staff.

Doulas do not provide the following services: vaginal exams, listening to fetal heart tones and taking blood pressure.

III.   **Responsibilities of the Client:**

Client agrees to inform her doctor or midwife that she has hired a Doula. Client also agrees to keep in contact with Doula after each doctor or midwife's visit, keeping her well informed of Client's medical condition, including any test results, and so that Doula may answer any questions that Client may have. Client agrees to provide Doula with a copy of her birth plan. Client agrees to participate in childbirth classes independent of the hospital, birth center, doctor or midwife. She further agrees to call Doula at the onset of labor and at lest one and one half hours before she would like Doula to arrive at her home or birth site.

IV.   **Failure of Doula to Provide Service**

Doula will make every reasonable effort to provide the services described here. If both Doula and Doula's back-up fail to attend Client's birth sue to Doula's fault, there will be no charge and Doula will refund the entire fee. If Doula of Doula's back-up fail to attend the Client's birth due to circumstances beyond their control (example: extremely rapid labor, restrictions by Hospital Staff, failure to call Doula, acts of God), Doula will retain the fee.

V.   **Fees**

Client shall pay the Doula a flat fee of $(amount) to provide the above-described services. One half of which (a non-refundable deposit) has been paid upon signing of this agreement and the balance is due by the 36th week of the pregnancy. If the fee has not been paid in full, Doula is not obligated to be present at the birth. Should either party decide to terminate this Agreement before the birth, the deposit will be retained by Doula, with the balance, if any, being returned to Client. If, for any reason, Client delivers baby with no primary care provider in attendance and the assistance of Doula, there will be a separate fee charged of $(amount) to cover the additional services provided. This fee would be due at the time of the birth.

Agreed and accepted this ___ day of _____, 19_____.

_____   _____
Client   Doula

_____
Client's Partner

Doula Client Letter and Contract
Crystal Sada whose Helping Hand Doula Service is based in Mt. Holly, New Jersey uses both this client letter and contract.

Date
Client Name and Address

It was a pleasure to meet with you to discuss your upcoming birth and how my services as a labor support doula could be beneficial to you. Enclosed please find two copies of an agreement which I drew up based on our conversation.

I suggest that everything we discussed for your birth al be discussed in detail with your physician/midwife. It was my impression from our conversation that you had already discussed most of your desires and with them.

If you are in agreement with what is presented here, please sign one copy and return to me with a deposit of $_____ . Should you decide to cancel the service the deposit will be retained. The second copy is for your records.

I look forward to meeting with you for our second session. If you have any questions before then please feel free to call.

Sincerely,

Helping Families Form Loving Bonds

This agreement between _____Client and Partner_____ and _____Doula_____ is for labor support services for the birth of their child. Their primary caregiver is _____Physician/Midwife_____.

The purpose of this agreement is so that all parties involved have an understanding of the function of a labor support doula and that the doula understands the needs and desires of the laboring couple.

It is also understood that during labor, situations could arise that make it medically necessary to perform certain interventions at the discretion of the medical staff for the safety of mother and/or baby. Although this is rare, it is not the doula's place to interfere with these decisions, but to continue to give both physical and emotional support and to help explain any procedures that may need to be performed.   It is the responsibility of the client and her partner to communicate with their physician/midwife as to the type of birth experience they desire. At the time of the birth the doula can and will remind the medical staff of those desires when or if necessary.

The doula does not provide medical care of any type but is available to offer suggestions and continuous comfort measures to the laboring couple with the approval of the attending physician/midwife.

Objectives:
1.   To deliver vaginally.
2.   To deliver unmedicated if possible. If anesthesia is necessary it is the desire of the client to have an _____type of anesthesia_____.
3.   The client would like to stay at home as long as possible as long as everything is proceeding normally. The doula will be present if requested but does NOT perform vaginal exams or fetal heart checks.
4.   Client has requested no episiotomy unless necessary for the health of the fetus. The doula, partner or medical staff will apply warm compresses and perform perineal massage during the pushing stage.
5.   Client would like a mirror available for either a vaginal or cesarean birth.
6.   Client would like to have her infant placed directly on her abdomen immediately after birth and would like to start breastfeeding.
7.   Partner would like to participate by cutting the cord.
8.   Cord blood banking is requested by the client and her partner have sent information to their physician about this process.
9.   Partner will act as primary support with Crystal offering suggestions, emotional and physical support, and acting as primary support when partner needs a break or to rest.

10.   FLEXIBILITY was agreed by all to be the most important factor for all the above objectives.

This agreement does not serve as a formal birth plan but as a guideline and reminder to be used during labor by the labor support doula.

Fees agreed upon are $_____   A deposit of $_____ will be due upon the signing of this agreement. Balance is due within two weeks of delivery. Should this agreement be broken within one month of delivery the client and partner forfeit the deposit.

Date
Client Name
Partner Name
Doula Name

Application for Employment
Equal access to programs, services and employment is available to all persons.

Please Print

Name_____

      Last   First   Middle

Address_____

      Street   City   State   ZIP

Telephone
Number_____

Social Security
Number_____

Position applied for _____Date of application_____

How were you referred to this
program?_____

Date available to work _____Salary desired_____

Type of employment desired_____Fulltime_____Part-time
_____Temporary

Are you able to meet the attendance requirements for this
position?_____

Are you eligible for employment in this country?_____Yes _____No
(Proof of US citizenship or immigaration status will be required.)

Have you ever been convicted of a felony?_____Yes_____No
If yes,
explain._____

Skills and Qualifications

Summarize your training, skills, certification, or licensure that may qualify you as being able to perform job-related functions in the position for which you are applying.

_____
_____
_____

Educational Background

Name and Location	Years Completed	Did you graduate?	Course of Study
High School			
College			
Other			

Employment History
List your last three employers, assignments or volunteer activities starting from the most recent.

Employer Name, Address and Phone	Dates Employed From To	Summarize the nature of your work and job responsibilities.
May we contact for reference?		
May we contact for reference?		
May we contact for reference?		

Signature of
Applicant_____Date_____

Labor and Delivery
Doula Peer Evaluation

Dear _____

Please complete the following review for _____ and return to our office as soon as possible.

Please rate the performance of the doula applicant on the following criteria using the rating system and definitions of the performance appraisal.

4-Exceeds criteria
3-Meets criteria
2-Needs Improvement
1-Unsatisfactory

Doula Process

1. _____ Maintains continuity of care for client
2. _____ Adheres to non-medical applications
3. _____ Uses appropriate infection control measures
4. _____ Works collaboratively with the healthcare team
5. _____ Provides appropriate physical comfort measures to the client
6. _____ Uses supportive emotional techniques that are helpful to the client
7. _____ Guides clients in making their own decisions
8. _____ Does not make decisions for the client
9. _____ Develops a sense for what techniques are appropriate at what times
10. _____ Is assertive in providing client care

Interpersonal Skills

Effective and appropriate verbal and non-verbal communication skills are practiced with

_____ peers (of the doulas)
_____ nurses
_____ midwives
_____ physicians
_____ laboring moms
_____ spouse or significant other
_____ family and friends
_____ Is available to help nurses, physicians, and midwives meet client needs
_____ Relays client requests to nursing staff in a respectful, tactful manner
_____ Asks client's permission to give verbal and touch support
_____ Asks for client information and background before assisting client

Quality Assessment and Improvement

_____ Offers ideas and suggestions for labor unit growth and development in a positive manner

_____ Shares concerns related to hospital, unit, client care in a constructive manner

_____ Clients offer comments indicating they are satisfied with the care they received.

_____ Performs activities demonstrating concern for client, peers, healthcare workers and own safety (i.e.: proper transfer/tilting techniques)

_____ Maintains client confidentiality

_____ Arrives within reasonable time from being called in

_____ Announces arrival and departure to staff

Accountability

_____ Subtle and overt changes in client's condition are reported to the nurse

_____ Maintains steady attention to the client

_____ Is able to organize and prioritize care to accommodate changes

_____ Handles unexpected changes or tense situations appropriately

_____ Helps client to remain calm when encountering difficult situations

Professional Growth Accountability

_____ Conducts self professionally to supporting peers, supervisors, and physicians

_____ Has a positive work attitude and is a pleasure to work with

_____ Works in a productive manner

_____ Is interested in continuing education

      _____ attends meetings

      _____ reads professional journals and books

      _____ asks questions

      _____ attends continuing education seminars

Charge Nurse Evaluation for a Hospital-Based Doula Program
Developed by Cheri Grant for a volunteer labor companion program in Tulsa, Oklahoma
used with permission

Charge Nurse:
Volunteer Doula:
Date:

What were the doula's strong points during the labor?
What would you like the doula to do differently next time?
Did the doula support the partner and other family members present?
Would you ask her to change anything about her appearance or personal hygiene?
During labor, was there anything said or done that bothered you?
Would you recommend the doula services to other patients?
Was the doula comfortable around you?
Did the doula show enthusiasm, senstivity and respect for you and the other hospital staff?
Did the doula respect and accept suggestions made by the staff?
After the baby was born, did the doula stay for an appropriate amount of time postpartum?

Please feel free to add any additional comments.

Hospital Doula Code of Ethics

Each doula shall sign and adhere to a professional code of ethics. This code of ethics is a modification of the DONA code of ethics to reflect a hospital-based program.

I.   **Rules of Conduct**

A.   Propriety

The doula shall maintain high standards of personal conduct in the capacity or identity as a labor support provider.

B.   Competence/Professional Development

The doula should strive to become and remain proficient in the professional practice of labor support and the performance of professional functions through continuing education, affiliation with related organizations and associations with other labor support providers.

C.   Integrity

The doula should act in accordance with the highest standards of professional integrity.

II.   **Ethical Responsibility to Clients**

A.   Client Interest

The doula's primary responsibility is to her clients, without jeopardizing medical safety.

B.   Client Rights

The doula must make every effort to foster self decision making on the part of her clients.

C.   Confidentiality

The doula will respect the privacy of her clients and hold in confidence all information obtained in the course of professional service.

D.   Obligation

The doula will be obligated to continue care as set up in the standards of practice of this program once professional support has started.

III. **Ethical Responsibility**

The doula will treat all members of the birth team with respect, courtesy, fairness and good faith. Conflicts and/or differences in opinion will not be discussed in the presence of the laboring woman.

IV.   **Ethical Responsibility to the Labor Support Profession**

A.   Maintenance and Advancement

The doula shall uphold and advance the values, ethics, knowledge and mission of the practice of professional labor support.

B.   Community Awareness

The doula will continue to work toward measures of increasing public awareness about the benefits of professional labor support.

V.   Societal Responsibility
The doula shall promote the general health and well being of women and their infants and extend this responsibility to their families whenever possible.

Volunteer Doula Program Code of Ethics
This is the code of ethics developed by Cheri Grant, R.N.
for a volunteer hospital-based doula program.

If accepted into the volunteer program I agree to:
Hold as absolutely confidential all information that I may obtain directly or indirectly concerning patient and staff and not seek to obtain confidential information.

Become familiar with the policies and procedures of the doula program and the hospital birth unit and uphold its philosophy and standards.

Donate my services to the doula program without compensation or contemplation of further employment.

Be punctual and conscientious, conduct myself with dignity, courtesy, and consideration of others and endeavor to make my work professional in quality.

Maintain a professional appearance while on my volunteer service.

Carry out assignments and seek the assistance of my supervisor when necessary.

Take any problems, criticism, or suggestions to my doula program coordinator or the designated nursing supervisor.

Adhere to the established rules and roles of the volunteer doula program.

Find a shift substitute, if ever necessary.

Honor my commitment toward volunteer service with the first three months being a probationary period.

Follow-up with the family as a doula program volunteer, giving the family a hospital visit, developmental calendar, booklet, pamphlet with the doula's name and phone number on it and contact by phone for up to three months.

Make one doula program postpartum visit during the first month.

Stay for the entire delivery until mom and baby are settled.

A volunteer who is also a professional doula may not have clients at the hospital and be a volunteer labor companion.

I understand that the hospital and the doula program reserves the right to terminate my volunteer services status at any time or as a result of:
a. Failure to comply with the hospital or program policies, rules and regulations;
b. Unsatisfactory attitude, work, or appearance;
c. Any other circumstances which, in the judgment of the department director or doula program coordinator, would make my continued services as a volunteer contrary to the best interests of the patients we serve and the hospital.

I have read each of the above conditions, and agree to be bound by them.

Volunteer's Signature and Date
Designated Nursing Supervisor
Doula Program Coordinator

Non-Profit Doula Program Ethics and Standards of Practice

Childbirth Enhancement Foundation, a non-profit program, has developed
the following ethics and standards of practice for its program.
used with permission

The Childbirth Enhancement Foundation maintains a set of ethical statements of practice to ensure that our clients receive quality service. A Childbirth Assistant working with CEF has a responsibility to her clients, her colleagues and to CEF. When working with a CEF client, a CEF CA, or CA intern is a representative of CEF and must adhere to the following standards.

Standards of Conduct and Appearance

1. In order to remain certified and stay active, a CEF CA must be a member in good standing of CEF, with all dues or fees paid, and an active CEF file. CA's are also expected to attend meetings in their area when scheduled, work within and adhere to the standards and ethical practices presented here, and participate in supervisory reviews as called for by the director of the Board of Directors.
2. In order to work with CEF clients or to display certification from CEF as a part of one's credentials as a CA, a CA must remain certified and active with CEF as specified in item 1, above.
3. A CEF CA should remain current on information and practices in the birth fields. Continuing education, affiliations with related organizations, and contact with other Childbirth Assistants or Doulas is encouraged.
4. A CEF CA cannot enter in to contracts on behalf of The Foundation. A CA is an agent of The Foundation, not an employee.
5. A CEF CA must maintain high standards of personal conduct and integrity in her capacity as a CEF representative.
6. A CEF CA must dress in a manner that is appropriate and professional in appearance. Blue jeans, shorts, and any clothing that is torn or stained are not appropriate. Scrubs, or comparable "birth clothes" are appropriate during labor and birth support.

Ethical Standards for Childbirth Assistants

1. A CEF CA's first responsibility is to her CEF clients. When working with a CEF client, a CEF CA must follow the Foundation's Ethical Standards.
2. A CEF CA shall do her best to make her clients aware of their rights; to help them understand those rights and what their CEF CA will or will not do on their behalf.
3. A CEF CA must follow confidentiality practices in relation to her clients, respect their privacy and hold in confidence all information obtained in the course of professional service, except in the circumstances of situations specified for release of information.

4. A CEF CA shall use discretion when discussing her clients with other professionals as specified in the release of information, and should not divulge information unrelated to the situation at hand. It is necessary to keep in mind that anything said about a client could also be heard by the client or her family.

5. A CEF CA **shall not** discuss clients by name with other clients, friends or acquaintances. A CEF CA may discuss clients by name with other professionals, as specified in the Contract for Service and Release of Information form. The CA should make every effort to protect the privacy of her clients, and should avoid using identifying names or information when using a case for teaching purposes with other professionals, or when casually discussing a specific case with anyone else.

6. A CEF CA who feels she cannot appropriately assist her client for any reason, including a personal conflict or fundamental difference in outlook, should discuss the matter with her supervisor or the Director and, as appropriate, with her client before making referrals to find the client other appropriate support.

7. Once a CEF CA has contracted with a CEF client, her obligation is to do so reliably and without fail for the duration of the contract. In the case on an emergency, an unforeseeable conflict or circumstances beyond the CA's control, she should provide an appropriate backup for the client. A CEF CA should help her client to acquire labor support either by providing it, or by making referrals to the appropriate resources.

8. When assessing a potential Foundation's client's ability to pay a sliding share of costs to CEF, a CEF CA should refer the potential client to The Foundation's main office for financial screening. The client's ability to pay shall be assessed by the CEF main office without bias for or against her. The main office will conduct the assessments and render a decision.

9. During a CA's internship, she shall not charge a fee for any services she reports to the Foundation for internship credit. Paid births may not be counted toward the internship requirements without prior arrangement with the Foundation.

10. All CA's (including interns) may accept small gifts from their clients, and may accept reimbursement for expenses incurred during or in relation to the client's labor and birth, if offered. (For example: parking fees, baby-sitting fees, travel expenses, etc.)

Childbirth Assistant's Responsibility to Colleagues and her Profession

1. A CEF CA should treat all colleagues with respect, fairness and courtesy. The actions of a CEF CA reflect on her professional appearance, her clients, CEF, and on the profession as a whole. A CEF CA should act ethically and honestly in all things. A CEF CA should uphold and advance the values, ethics, knowledge and mission of the profession of CA or Doula.

2. If a CEF CA has contact with the clients of a colleague, she should give them full professional consideration and should follow any plans the client has established with the colleague to the best of her ability.

3. As appropriate, a CEF CA should promote the profession as a whole and help to provide knowledge and information about it to her community. A CA can promote the general health of women, children and families as well as the specific health and well being of her clients.

4. The Foundation does not discriminate against its clients, CA's or board members on the basis of their race, religion, gender or age. A CEF CA shall not deny services to any client based on any of these reasons.

5. The Foundation certifies CAs based on The Foundation's training and certification program. This includes **no** certification in, or endorsement of any CA's obstetrical assessment skills. While some CA's may have experience with clinical skills relating to the birthing process, and may even have degrees relating to those skills, they are **not** certified in them by CEF, and are **not permitted** to use them when working as a CEF CA.

By signing below I acknowledge that I understand these ethics and standards as they relate to my work with CEF. I realize that if I do not follow the ethics and standards stated here, my certification from CEF may be jeopardized, suspended or taken from me by the Foundation.

Childbirth Assistant   Date   CEF Witness   Date

Doulas of North America Code of Ethics
Used with permission.

I.   Rules of Conduct

A. Propriety. The doula should maintain high standards of personal conduct in the capacity or identity of Professional Labor Support Provider.

B. Competence and Professional Development. The doula should strive to become and remain proficient in the professional practice and the performance of professional functions through continuing education, affiliation with related organizations, and associations with other Labor Support Providers.

C. Integrity. The doula should act in accordance with the highest standards of professional integrity.

II.   Ethical Responsibility to Clients

A. Primacy of Client's Interests. The doula's primary responsibility is to her clients.

B. Rights and Prerogatives of Clients. The doula should make every effort to foster maximum self-determination on the part of her clients.

C. Confidentiality and Privacy. The doula should respect the privacy of clients and hold in confidence all information obtained in the course of professional service.

D. Obligation to Serve. The doula should assist each client seeking labor support either by providing services or making appropriate referrals.

E. Reliability. When the doula agrees to work with a particular client, her obligation is to do so reliably, without fail, for the term of the agreement.

F. Fees. When setting fees, the doula should ensure that they are fair, reasonable, considerate, and commensurate with service performed and with due regard for the client's ability to pay.

III.   Ethical Responsibility to Colleagues

A. Respect, Fairness, and Courtesy. The doula should treat colleagues with respect, courtesy, fairness, and good faith.

B. Dealing with Colleagues' Clients. The doula has the responsibility to relate to the clients of colleagues with full professional consideration.

IV.   Ethical Responsibility to the Labor Support Profession

A. Maintaining the Integrity of the Profession. The doula should uphold and advance the values, ethics, knowledge and mission of the profession.

B. Community Service. The doula should assist the profession in making labor support services available to the general public.

V.   Ethical Responsibility to Society

A. Promoting Maternal and Child Welfare. The doula should promote the general health of women and their babies, and whenever possible, that of their family and friends as well.

Doulas of North America Standards of Practice
Used with permission.

I. Scope

A. Services Rendered. The doula accompanies the woman in labor, provides emotional and physical support, suggests comfort measures, and provides support and suggestions for the partner. Whenever possible, the doula provides pre and postpartum emotional support, including explanation and discussion of practices and procedures, as needed.

B. Limits to Practice. The doula does not perform clinical or medical tasks such as taking blood pressure or temperature, fetal heart tone checks, vaginal examinations or postpartum clinical care. DONA Standards and Certification apply to emotional and physical support only. Doulas who are also healthcare professionals may provide these services within the scope and standards of practice of their professions.

C. Advocate. The doula advocates for the client's wishes as expressed in her birth plan, in prenatal conversations, and intrapartum discussion. She helps the mother incorporate changes in plans if and when the need arises, and enhances communication between client and caregiver. Clients and doulas must recognize that the advocacy role does not include the doula speaking on behalf of the client or making decisions for the client. The advocacy role is best described as support, information, and mediation or negotiation.

II. Continuity of Care

The doula should make back-up arrangements with another doula to ensure services to the client if the doula is sick or unable to be reached. Should any doula feel a need to discontinue service to an established client, it is the doula's responsibility to notify the client in writing and arrange for a replacement, if the client so desires. This may be accomplished by:

A. Introducing the client to the doula's back-up.

B. Suggestion that another member of DONA or other doula may be more appropriate for the situation.

C. Contacting DONA Regional Representative for local doula organization for names of other doulas in the area.

D. Following up with client or back-up doula to make sure the client's needs are being accommodated.

III. Training and Experience

A. Training. Doulas who are certified by DONA will have completed all the requirements as set forth in the DONA Requirements for Certification. This includes a high school diploma or the equivalent, training in childbirth and a labor support course which consists of at least fourteen hours of training, read four books from the DONA reading list, and completion of an essay on the value and purpose of labor support.

B. Experience. Doulas certified by DONA will have the experience as set forth in the DONA Requirements for Certification. This includes provision of support to al least three clients, good evaluations from clients and healthcare providers, and records of three births, including a summary, observation form and accounts for each birth.

C. Maintenance of Certification. DONA certified doulas will maintain certification by participation in a Peer Review process after each three-year period of practice. Doulas must attend at least one continuing education event per year in maternal/child heath.

IV.   Record Keeping

A. Documentation. The doula maintains clear and accurate records of each client encounter and the birth.

B. Data Collection. The doula collects and submits to DONA on a regular basis data on the clients she provides services to, and the outcome of their pregnancies and labors.

Standards of Practice
Hospital-Based Doula Program

Each doula shall sign and adhere to a methodology for standards of practice. This document is modified from the DONA standards of practice for a hospital-based program.

I.   **Scope**

A.   Services Rendered

The doula program is optional. Each woman will be given the information regarding the doula program and will be free to elect or decline the program.   The doula will accompany the woman in labor, provide continuous emotional and physical support, suggest comfort measures, provide positive encouragement, as well as provide support and suggestions for the partner/spouse or other family members and friends in attendance. Within the confines of employment of this hospital, the doula will provide pre and postpartum emotional support, including discussion of practices and procedures and referrals for additional information.

B.   Limits to Practice

The doula does not perform clinical or medical tasks such as taking blood pressure or temperature, fetal heart tone checks, vaginal examinations or postpartum clinical care. Standards of practice pertain to emotional and physical support only. If employed in a different healthcare position (labor and delivery nurse) these standards will apply when functioning in the doula role.

C.   Advocacy

The doula's primary role is to support the laboring woman's wishes. She may help the mother to incorporate changes in her birth plan if and when the need arises. The doula should enhance communication between the client and caregivers.   Clients and doulas must recognize the doula support role does not include speaking on behalf of the client or making decisions for the client. The doula role is best described as support and information and a clarifying liaison.

D.   Referrals

For client needs and questions beyond the scope of the doula, referrals are made to appropriate resources.

II.   **Continuity of Care**

The doula will be on-call for a specific amount of hours (to be determined by the individual institution). It is the responsibility of the doula to be available during any period of this scheduled on-call time. Exceptions are made for illness or emergencies. It is the responsibility of the doula to notify the doula program director if the above circumstances become relevant during any period in which she is providing care or prior to providing care. If providing support at a birth extends beyond the call time, it is the responsibility of the doula to continue with care until the birth of the baby and all subsequent needs have been met.

III. Training and Experience
A. Training
Doulas must meet the following minimal requirements or be certified by a doula/birth assistant certifying body (DONA, ALACE, ICEA, etc.).

For those doulas not certified, training will be provided with prerequisites of the following: a high school diploma or equivalent; attendance at a comprehensive childbirth education series; required reading from our specified list; and written evaluations of births attended with a preceptor.

Each doula will be required to become certified in labor support within (state time frame).

B. Experience
Doula experience is not necessary. More important is the criteria of unconditional support and commitment to the laboring woman. Experience in working in "team" situations can be considered an advantage.

C. Maintenance in Good Standing
After certification, doulas must maintain their certification by adhering to the requirements of their certifying organization. Doulas may make application for different or additional certification, but it is not required. Continuing education may be offered by the hospital at designated times.

IV. Record Keeping
A. Documentation
The doula will not document anything on the patient's chart. Documentation of pertinent information will be made available onsite for the doula in advance of meeting with the client so that she may familiarize herself with any specifics regarding the laboring woman. The doula will only document in and out times, patient name, address, phone, baby's name, weight, length, time of birth along with a recap of the labor and birth to be given to the client as a birth keepsake. One copy will be kept in the doula program office. All followup visits will also be documented.

Letters to Third Party Payors
Crystal Sada, a New Jersey doula uses this letter
to help her clients receive third party reimbursement.
Used with permission.

As a certified nursing assistant in maternity for eight years, and a certified childbirth educator for fourteen years, I recently became certified to offer support to women in labor. It is my feeling that insurance companies could benefit by providing reimbursement to women for the services of a labor support professional, herein referred to as a "doula."

Numerous articles and books have been published about the benefits of a doula. Just this past year *JAMA* featured an article on this subject. My position is if insurance companies paid this fee, or a portion thereof, they could save a great deal of money. There are several excellent books on this subject. One very well noted book, *Mothering the Mother*, is written by Marshall Klaus, MD, John Kennell, MD, and Phyllis Klaus, M.Ed. CSW. In 1976 Marshall Klaus and John Kennell authored *Maternal Infant Bonding, The Impact of Early Separation or Loss on Family Development.* This book helped to revolutionize the way infants were treated after delivery, including premature infants. Since this time we have come to realize that even the most delicate premature infants need hands-on contact in order to grow and thrive, which in turn cuts down on the number of days spent hospitalized, which in turns saves insurance dollars.

In their book, *Mothering the Mother*, Klaus, Kennell, and Klaus provide some very concrete statistics concerning the effect of doulas on the labor and delivery patterns of women.   the following are statistics taken from this publication.

1. Interventions: Women who are provided a doula have less incidence of intervention, which includes the need for medications such as analgesics and epidurals; less chance of cesarean birth, and are more successful at delivering vaginally following a previous cesarean than women who do not have this service offered.

2. Medications: 50% reduction in the use of medications, including epidurals. In one study of 416 women, 55% of the women not utilizing a doula received an epidural, while only 8% of women utilizing a doula received an epidural.

3. Pitocin: 44% needed pitocin to augment labor. Only 17% of the women utilizing a doula required pitocin.

4. Forceps: 26% of women not utilizing a doula required a forceps delivery, while only 8% of those utilizing a doula required forceps.

5. Newborn Hospitalization: Newborns hospitalized after delivery (kept for more than two days) was 24% without a doula, as opposed to only 10% with a doula.

6. Maternal Hospitalization: Women usually felt more confident about leaving the hospital within 24 hours than women who did not have a doula. This is felt to be the result of the doula working with the family and providing education and telephone contact for support after the delivery.

Considering that one intervention leads to another, which ultimately can lead to a cesarean (the Domino Effect) and a longer stay for both mother and infant, the cost to an insurance company for the services of a doula is minuscule.

As an example, the fee I usually charge is $400.00 for the entire labor, which includes going to the home for early labor so that hospitalization does not occur until labor is well established. In the 14 births I have attended in the past calendar year, only one ended in cesarean, and I just recently had a client who developed pre-eclampsia and still successfully delivered vaginally. One woman accepted an epidural after 24 hours of a pitocin-induced labor. All women except the one with pre-eclampsia and the cesarean birth went home within 24 hours, even though in the state of New Jersey they have the option of hospitalization for 48 hours.

Women who have doula care during labor and the post-partum adjustment period have less post-partum depression than women who are not provided this service and have no one to care for them.

I feel strongly that insurance companies should offer this service. Most women I provide services to are fortunate enough to have the ability to pay this cost out of pocket, My concern is for women who do not have the resources to afford this service. These are usually the women who are most at risk for not only interventions and cesareans, but also post-partum depression as well.

In most cases the doula does not provide medical care unless she/he is a Registered Nurse and is then referred to as a Monitrice. However, having worked in a hospital setting, most nurses in labor and delivery cannot provide one-on-one care for the duration of the labor. The doula stays with the woman throughout the entire labor, providing physical and emotional comfort measures to encourage labor to progress quicker and safer without intervention.

I strongly urge insurance companies to provide reimbursement to women for the services of a doula, much like insurance companies now reimburse for childbirth education classes. Many innovative insurance companies have already started to reimburse for this service, or to hire doulas to participate in the birth of their subscribers. Either way, the insurance company, and laboring women, are the beneficiaries of this type service.

If you would like, I could send you detailed information about the methods I utilize to help women succeed in labor.

Prenatal Interview
This form can be used when interviewing prospective clients.
Used with permission.

Client's
Name:_____

Partner's
Name:_____

Address:_____

Home Phone:_____

Pager:_____

Her Work #_____   His Work#:_____

OB/Midwife:_____phone:_____

Hospital:_____phone:_____

Pediatrician:_____phone:_____

Due Date:_____Client's Birth date:_____

I.   **Health History**

1.   Please describe your health in general (pre-pregnancy)

2.   Blood Type
3.   Drug allergies or reactions

4.   Any chronic illnesses

5.   List any medications you take regularly

6.   List any surgeries along with date of treatment

7.   List any infertility treatments along with date of procedures

8.   List any emotional disorders along with date of onset & types of treatment

9.   Do you have any concerns about your well-being?

II.   **Childbearing History**

1.   Have you had any childbearing losses? (i.e. abortion, miscarriage, infertility, stillbirth or children placed for adoption)

2.   Vital information on previous births (i.e. date, gender, name and birth weight)

3.   How did labor begin? How long did it last? How did you push? What coping techniques did you use?

4.   Were there any complications?

5.   What was the best thing about the experience? What element would you hope to avoid this time?

III.   **Anticipated Birth**

1.   How is your pregnancy going? Is it what you expected?

2.   Are you feeling rested? Restless? Any interesting dreams?

3.   Have there been any problems with this pregnancy? If so, what?

4.   Which prenatal tests, if any, have you had? Results?

5.   What childbirth education have you taken?

6.   Who have you chosen to be with you during this birth and what role will each person play?

7.   Have you told your doctor that you are hiring labor support?

8.   How do you imagine I can be most helpful to you?

        Client:

        Client's Partner:

9.   Imagine your ideal birth. What makes it ideal?

        Client:

        Client's Partner:

10.   Have you completed your birth plan? May I have a copy?

11.   What are the 3 most vital elements of your birth plan (in order of importance)?

        Client:

        1.

        2.

        3.

        Client's Partner:

        1.

        2.

        3.

12.   What are your greatest fears about this birth?

        Client:

        Client's Partner:

13.   In the event of an unanticipated c-section, what things would be most important to you?

14.   What are the most stressful aspects of your life? How do you counteract this stress?

15.   What is your occupation? Partner's?

16.   Have you experienced any significant losses (i.e. death of a parent, sibling, divorce, loss of birth family through adoption, etc.)

17.   Have you had any other life traumas? (i.e. physical, emotional, sexual, or substance abuse)

18.   Who do you turn to for support?

19.   Tell me about a time when you felt especially calm. What were the circumstances?

20.   Tell me about a time when you felt especially powerful. What were the circumstances?

21.   In general, where do you feel tension in your body? (i.e. head, neck, chest, shoulders, jaw, legs, back, etc.)and how to do your manifest that tension? (i.e. racing heart, difficulty breathing, nail biting, nausea, grinding teeth, clenched fists, etc.)

22.   In painful situations, how do you seek comfort? (i.e. companionship, activity, quiet, turning inward, making noise, rhythmic movement, distraction, etc.)

23.   When frightened, how do you regain a sense of calmness? (i.e. deep breathing, deliberate relaxation, reassurance from others, visualization, information gathering, etc.)

24.   In labor, what coping techniques do you anticipate using? (i.e. walking, music, nature sound machine, relaxation, shower/bath, massage, rocking, position changes, encouragement, moaning, visualization, etc.)

25.   What provisions for photographing the birth have you made?

IV.   Newborn

1.   Do you know the gender of this baby? If so, how?

2.   What do you plan on naming this baby?

3.   In ideal circumstances, how would you like to welcome your baby? (i.e., non-separation, immediate nursing, hear your voice first, etc.)

4.   Do you plan on nursing?

5.   If mother & baby need to be separated, who should remain with mom, who should remain with baby?

6.   Do you plan on circumcising this child if it is male?

7.   Do you have any special concerns about your child?

V.   Logistical Plan
1.   How would you like to pay my fee? (½ when hired & ½ due by 36 weeks)

2.   How often shall we be in touch?

3.   When shall I come in labor (2 hours advance notice needed)

4.   How far along would you like to be when we leave for/arrive at hospital?

5.   Call me anytime, page as needed (put in the numbers 911 following your phone number for an emergency page)

BIRTH LOG

CLIENT NAME _____ BABY'S NAME_____ SEX_____
DATE _____TIME LABOR BEGAN _____TIME OF BIRTH _____BIRTHSITE _____
APGAR SCORE _____BABY'S WEIGHT _____BABY'S LENGTH _____
NURSE _____CAREGIVER _____ BABY'S DOCTOR _____

STAGE OF LABOR	CLIENT'S FEELINGS	COPING MEASURES USED	EVENTS	COMMENTS
EARLY LABOR				
ACTIVE LABOR				
TRANSITION				
PUSHING/2ND STAGE				
BIRTH				
POSTPARTUM				

SAMPLE

Cheri B. Grant • M & W Productions • Tulsa, Oklahoma • 1/94

Postpartum Visit Questions

It is helpful if all doulas ask the same basic questions and then expand on these questions according to the feedback that they receive from the new mother.

1.   How much sleep have you been getting?
2.   What type and amount of support do you have at home?
3.   What are your feelings/memories regarding your birth experience?
4.   What did you find most helpful during your labor and birth?
5.   What, if anything, would you change about the experience?
6.   What, if anything, would you have changed about the labor support during your labor and birth?
7.   What, if anything, would you change at your next birth?

Doula Postpartum Follow-Up Visit

Doula_____

Client_____

Date of birth_____

Address_____

Phone_____

Baby_____Name_____

__Sex

Dates of phone

calls_____

Time

Spent_____

Briefly describe telephone conversations

_____

_____

_____

_____

Date of Personal

Visit_____

Time

Spent_____

Briefly describe the personal visit

_____

_____

_____

_____

_____

_____

_____

Your Birth Story

Written by your
doula_____

A baby_____named_____

was born on_____at_____weighing_____

Labor lasted _____ Those in attendance were:

Doctor_____

Midwife_____

Nurses_____

Doula_____ Family & Friends_____

Mom's Name_____ Dad's Name_____

Where You
Lived_____
                        Address

Special Birth
Memories_____

_____
_____
_____
_____
_____
_____
_____
_____
_____
_____
_____
_____
_____
_____
_____
_____
_____
_____
_____
_____
_____
_____
_____
_____
_____
_____
_____
_____
_____
_____
_____
_____

Doula Program Marketing Tool

(Program Name)'s doulas provide a supportive *continuous presence* during your birthing experience.

The extra measure of support you will receive are:

- Massage
- Assistance with positioning
- Encouragement, guidance and support for mom and partner
- Assistance with relaxation techniques
- Comfort Measures
- Assistance with breathing techniques

Picture   (Name) is the coordinator of the doula program.
                              She is a (certified doula, certified childbirth Educator)
                              She has attended more than (#) births, (#) lectures, on maternity care and is a member
                              Of (professional organizations).

Picture and bio for each doula in the program.

To arrange for a doula or to obtain more information please call
        (Name in large print)
        (Program Phone Number in Large Print)

Value Identification

Please read all of the statements listed below and circle the four or five items that are most important to you.

1.   To be most attractive to others.
2.   Being an honest person.
3.   To have political power.
4.   Being known as a "real" person.
5.   Good self-confidence and personal growth.
6.   A life with meaning, purpose and fulfillment.
7.   Continuing to learn and gain knowledge.
8.   A chance to help women.
9.   Some honest and close relationships.
10.   A long and healthy life.
11.   A meaningful relationship with God.
12.   Satisfaction/success in my career of choice.
13.   A financially comfortable lifestyle.
14.   Accomplish something worthwhile.
15.   A secure and positive family life.
16.   An enjoyable, leisurely life.
17.   Being a "change" agent.
18.   A chance to develop creativity/potential in any area.
19.   To live up to my convictions.
20.   To be a good parent.
21.   To have a better relationship with my parents.
22.   To have better feelings about myself.
23.   To be needed and to be important to others.
24.   Owning a possession of great value.
25.   To persevere in what I am doing.
26.   To be secure monetarily.
27.   To give of myself freely in helping others.
28.   To be loved by a special few.
29.   To be an entrepreneur.

Please write the numbers of those statements you circled on the blanks below.

——— ——— ——— ——— ———

This form is adapted from the work of Patty Hendrickson and used with permission.

Value Identification Characteristics

Characteristics	Numbers Chosen	Number of Occurrences
Sincerity	4	_____
Honesty, integrity	2, 19	_____
Emotional well-being, stability	5, 22	_____
Education, intelligence, wisdom	7	_____
Altruism, fairness, justice	8, 27	_____
Love, friendship, closeness	9, 23, 28	_____
Health, fulfillment, productivity	10	_____
Religion, spirituality	11	_____
Family, love emotional security	15, 20, 21	_____
Fulfillment, intellectual & career achievement	6, 12, 14, 18, 25, 29	_____
Financial security, money, status	13, 24, 26	_____
Pleasure, travel, & material satisfaction	16	_____
Power, achievement	3, 17	_____

This form is adapted from the work of Patty Hendrickson and used with permission.

Team Values

Understanding the values of your team is important. It will help clarify the goals and priorities of your actions. Identify your team values by adding the number of times each characteristic was chosen by your team members.

Number of Occurrences

Sincerity

_____

Honesty, integrity

_____

Emotional well-being, stability

_____

Education, intelligence, wisdom

_____

Altruism, fairness, justice

_____

Love, friendship, personal closeness

_____

Health, fulfillment, productivity

_____

Religion, spirituality

_____

Family, love emotional security

_____

Fulfillment, intellectual &
career achievement

_____

Financial security, money, status

_____

Pleasure, travel, material satisfaction

_____

Power, achievement

_____

This form is adapted from the work of Patty Hendrickson and used with permission.

Doula Program Follow-up Survey

We would appreciate your taking a few minutes to complete the following survey. Your remarks will help us provide better service for all new mothers and their families. All your responses will be kept confidential. Please return the survey in the enclosed self-addressed, postage paid envelope. Thank you.

1.   What was the date of your baby's
     birth?_____

2.   What was the name of your
     physician/midwife?_____

3.   What was the name of your
     doula?_____

4.   Did you attend prenatal classes? (Check one.) _____ Yes _____No

5.   What is your age? _____Under 15 _____15-17 _____18-24 _____25-29
          ____ 30-34 _____ 35-39 ____ 40-44 _____ Over 45

6.   How many others beyond your doula were there to support you?
     _____ partner or spouse _____ parent _____ friend _____ other

7.   Please check all the services that were provided by your doula during the labor & birth.

_____ massage	_____ position changes	_____ cold/hot packs
_____ shower/bath	_____ acupressure	_____ counter pressure
_____ water/juice	_____ eased fears	_____ breathing techniques
_____ eye contact	_____ took photos	_____ followed my wishes
_____ verbal encouragement		_____ answered questions
_____ continuous presence		_____ double hip squeeze
_____ included other support people		_____ knee press
_____ helped my partner/spouse		_____ lunge
_____ reinforced birth ritual		_____ stomp-squat
_____ discussed my options		_____ ambulation
_____ other (please specify)		_____ labor ball

8.   Which services helped you the
     most?_____
     _____
     _____
     _____
     _____
     _____
     _____
     _____

9.   Any services that you did not like? (Please specify.)

_____

_____

_____

_____

10.   How well did your doula relate to you on a personal
        level?_____

        _____

11.   How did your doula interact with the other members of the birth team
        (physicians. Midwives, nurses, anesthesiologists). Check one.
        _____ Very well   _____ Sufficiently _____ Poorly

12.   Were you satisfied with the length of time your doula remained with you
        after the birth?_____ Yes _____ No
        Length of time she was there _____

13.   Did the follow up visit from your doula help you? Please explain.

        _____

        _____

        _____

        _____

14.   I felt that the fee I paid for the doula service was:
        _____ fair   _____ too high   _____ too low   _____ just right
        _____ I received insurance reimbursement for this service

15.   How did you learn about the doula program? (Check all that apply.)
        _____ brochure in physician/midwife office   _____ newspaper
        _____ brochure in hospital   _____ radio
        _____ prenatal classes   _____ television
        _____ friends   _____ prenatal exercise
                                                                class
        _____ open house   _____ midwife
        _____ physician   _____ nurse
        _____ doula   _____ other (please
                                                                specify)

Thank you for taking the time to assist us by providing your input. Return survey
in enclosed envelope.

Client Evaluation

Name:
Labor Companion Name:
Baby's Name:
Baby's Birth Date:
Dr.'s Name:

Please rate the Labor Companion's services on the following scale:

1	3	5
Not al all useful	Somewhat useful	Very useful

Emotional support in Labor
Tips and Techniques for Comfort in Labor
Visit
The Labor Companion was helpful to friends & family.
The labor Companion was knowledgeable.
The Labor Companion was sensitive & respectful.
What did you like about your Labor Companion?
Was there anything you would like to comment on? Please do so.

Would you recommend the Volunteer Labor Companion program to others?
Why or why not?

Bill Proposal

Section 1.   A licensed Birth Doula is a person who:
(1) Provides prenatal education to expectant parents.
(2) Provides emotional, physical, and informational support throughout labor and immediate postpartum
(3) Offers postpartum visits to facilitate the transition to parenthood

Section 2.   The Health Division will establish a State Board of Birth Doulas that shall consist of seven members. These members will be appointed by the Assistant Director for Health and will serve a term of three years until a successor is appointed and qualified. If, for any cause, there is a vacancy, the Assistant Director for Health shall make an appointment to become immediately effective for the remainder of that term.
The membership of the board shall include:
(1) Four licensed Birth Doulas
(2) One Registered Nurse
(3) One Obstetrician
(4) One Direct Entry Midwife

Section 3.   (1) The State Board of Birth Doulas shall establish standards for qualifications for the licensure of Birth Doulas. Such standards shall include, but are not limited to, the following:
(A) Sufficient knowledge of the following areas:
(a) Techniques of interviewing expectant parents for compatibility purposes
(b) Anatomy and physiology of the female reproductive system
(c) The mechanics of normal and pathological childbirth
(d) Effective communication techniques
(e) Physical and emotional ability to handle the demands of the position
(f) Lactation counseling techniques
(g) Early parenting counseling techniques
(h) The role of the Birth Doula
(i) Techniques employed by Birth Doulas that facilitate labor and delivery
(B) Successful passage of written and oral examinations; and
(C) Participation in:
(a) Observing two births with a licensed Doula attending the parents;
(b) Be observed by the same licensed Doula for three additional births;
(c)Attending two client's postpartum visits with a licensed Birth Doula;
(d) Written evaluations of each birth and postpartum visit from the attending Licensed Birth Doula

(e) Current certification in infant and adult cardiopulmonary resuscitation

(2) Any person who desires to become licensed as a Birth Doula shall submit an application to the board that states the applicant's qualifications for licensure. If the applicant meets the established standards under subsection (1) of this section and is not disqualified under section 10 of this bill proposal, the board shall issue an annual license to the Birth Doula. The board shall impose a fee for liensure and examinations. The fees shall be established at a rate that meets the administration costs of the program but shall not exceed $125 for initial licensure and $125 for renewal.

(3) Any person licensed to practice as a Birth Doula is entitled to payment under the rules of the medical assistance program for services provided to any eligible recipient of medical assistance.

Section 4. A person licensed to practice as a Birth Doula under the laws of another state who demonstrates to the satisfaction of the State Board of Birth Doulas that the person has passed a written examination at least equal to the written examination required of person eligible for licensure under this Bill Proposal may have the written examination waived pursuant to the standards of the board.

Section 5. The State Board of Birth Doulas shall keep a record of its proceedings relating to the issuance, refusal, suspension, and revocation of licenses. The board shall keep a record of all complaints received, including the date of receipt, name of licensee, name and address of each complainant and the nature of the complaint.

Section 6. (1) The State Board of Birth Doulas shall elect a chair person. The board shall adopt rules to govern the proceedings of the board. The board shall hold meetings at such times and places as it determines. A majority of the members of the board shall constitute a quorum.

(2) Each member of the board is entitled to compensation and expenses as provided from the revenue generated from license applications and renewals.

Section 7. In addition to the powers otherwise granted by this bill proposal, the State Board of Birth Doulas may:

(1) Determine whether applicants meet the qualifications under this bill proposal, conduct examinations and grant licenses to qualified applicants upon compliance with the rules of the board;

(2) Do any act necessary or proper to effect and carry out the duties required of the board by this bill proposal; and

(3) Adopt rules for the administration of this bill proposal.

Section 8. The State Board of Birth Doulas shall develop practice standards that shall include but are not limited to:

(1) Maintenance of statistical records of births with board approved forms;

(2) Participation in peer review;

(3) Maintenance of client disclosure forms, which includes information regarding whether the Doula has malpractice insurance.

Section 9.   (1) The State Board of Birth Doulas annually shall renew a license for a Birth Doula upon receipt of the renewal application and fee and proof of current cardiopulmonary certification for infants and adults, if the applicant is otherwise in compliance with the rules adopted by the board.

(2) The board shall establish the procedure for renewing licenses.

(3) The board shall prescribe requirements for license renewal including, but not limited to, continuing education.   In addition to continuing education requirements, a Birth Doula who has attended fewer than three births in the previous year shall be required to take additional hours of continuing education requirements as prescribed by the board.   The board shall all licensing requirements by rule.

(4) Any license that is not renewed at the end of the calendar year shall automatically revert to inactive status. The license may be reactivated only if the license holder meets other qualifications for reactivation as prescribed by the board by rule.

(5) Sixty days prior to the end of the calendar year, the board shall mail a notice of renewal to the last-known address of the license holder.

Section 10.   (1) The following acts shall be grounds for which the State Board of Birth Doulas may refuse to grant a license or may exercise disciplinary action against a licensed Birth Doula:

(a) Procuring, attempting to procure, renewing or attempting to renew a license to practice as a Birth Doula by bribery or fraudulent misrepresentation.

(b) Having a license to practice as a Birth Doula revoked, suspended or denied by the licensing authority of another state, territory or country.

(c) Being convicted of found guilty, in any jurisdiction that authorizes Birth Doulas to practice in that jurisdiction, of a crime that directly relates to the practice of Birth Doulas or to the ability to practice as a Birth Doula.

(d) Making or filing a false report or record that the license holder knows to be false, intentionally or negligently failing to file a report or record required by state or federal law, or willingly impeding or obstructing such filing or inducing another to do so. Reports or records shall include only reports or records that are signed in the Birth Doula's capacity as a licensed Birth Doula.

(e) Advertising falsely, misleadingly or deceptively.

(f) Engaging in unprofessional conduct including, but not limited to, any departure from or the failure to conform to the standards of practice of the Birth Doula as established by the board, in which case actual injury need not be established.

(g) Being unable to practice as a Birth Doula with reasonable skill and safety to patients by reason of illness or use of controlled substances, alcohol or other materials or as a result of any physical or mental impairment.   At reasonable intervals, a Birth Doula described in this paragraph shall be afforded an opportunity to demonstrate that the Birth Doula can resume competent practice with reasonable skill and safety.

(h) Willfully or repeatedly violating any provision of this bill proposal, any rule of the board or any lawful order of the board previously entered in a disciplinary proceeding.

(2) When the board finds any person has violated any grounds set forth in subsection (1) of this section, the board may take one of the following disciplinary actions:

(a) Refuse to approve an allocation for licensure.

(b) Revoke or suspend a license.

(c) Impose a civil penalty not to exceed $450.00 for each count or separate offense.

(d) Issue a reprimand.

(e) Place the Birth Doula on probation for a period of time and subject to conditions as the board may specify including, but not limited to, requiring the Birth Doula to:

(A) Undertake further relevant education and training.

(B) Take an examination

(C) Work under the supervision of another licensed Birth Doula for a prescribed time set forth by the board.

(3) The board shall not reinstate the license of a Birth Doula or cause a license to be issued to a person it considers unqualified until such time as the board is satisfied that the person has complied with all the terms and conditions set forth in subsection (2)(e) of this section and that the person is capable of safely engaging practice as a Birth Doula.

(4) The board shall establish guidelines for the disposition of disciplinary cases involving specific types of violations.

Section 11. (1) A license authorized by this bill proposal is required only for the purposes of reimbursement under medical assistance programs and is not required for practicing as a Birth Doula in this state.

(2) Nothing is this bill proposal is intended to require a Birth Doula to become licensed as described in section 3(2) of this bill proposal.

Section 12. (1) The Persons first appointed to the State Board of Birth Doulas under section (2) if this bill proposal are not required to be licensed as Birth Doulas but must be licensed to be qualified.

Section 13. (1) Notwithstanding the term of office specified by section2 of this bill proposal, of the members first appointed to the State Board of Birth Doulas:

(1) Four shall serve for a term ending June 30, 2001.

(2) Three shall serve a term ending June 30, 2002.

Section 14. (1) In cooperation with the State Board of Birth Doulas, the Health Division shall collect and report data on births for which a Birth Doula was present. The report shall distinguish outcomes between licensed Birth Doulas and Birth Doulas who are not licensed under this bill proposal.

Section 15 (1) No person shall use the title "Licensed Birth Doula", any abbreviation thereof or the initials "L.B.D." unless the person possesses a valid license issued under this bill proposal.

Section 16   (1) Any information provided to the State Board of Birth Doulas under section 10 of this bill proposal is confidential and shall not be subject to public disclosure or admissible as evidence in any judicial proceeding.

(3) Any person who in good faith provides information to the board shall not be subject to an action for civil damages as a result thereof.

Section 17   (1) The Assistant Director for Health shall fix the qualifications of and appoint an administrator for the State Board of Birth Doulas who shall not be a member of the board. Subject to applicable provisions of the State Personnel Relations Law, the assistant director shall fix the compensation of the administrator who shall be in the unclassified service.

(2). The assistant director shall provide the board with such services and employees as the board requires to carry out its duties.

Section 18   (1) Any Doula what holds a current certification by Doulas of North America may be exempt from:

(a) the written exam

(b) observing two births with a licensed Doula

(c)being observed by a licensed Doula for three additional births

(d) attending two postpartum visits with a licensed Doula

(e) submitting a written evaluation of births and postpartum visits

For further information about this bill proposal contact Kelly Precie at P.O. Box 204, Medford, OR 97501 (541/732-0548) or kellyprecie@wave.net
used with permission

Common Diagnostic
and
Current Procedural Terminology Codes

The original format for the ICD-9 was that of the World Health Organization and is widely used for reporting and assembling vital statistical information. Although there are often yearly changes in the codes, the basic system has been in place for 30 years. You may also access some of these codes on the Internet at http://www.icd-9-cm.org and they are available from the Government Printing Office by calling 202-512-1800 and referring to order number 017-022-01352-5.

Diagnostic Codes

V22.2	Intrauterine pregnancy
V24.2	Routine postpartum follow-up
V24.1	Lactation
V23.7	Poor Obstetrical History
V23.9	High Risk Pregnancy
V23.4	Poor obstetric history
661.3	Precipitous labor
648.80	Gestational Diabetes Mellitus
660.7	Failed forceps delivery
650	Normal vaginal delivery
660.71	Delivery with or without mention of antepartum condition
660.70	Unspecified
660.73	Antepartum condition
653.4	Cephalopelvic disproportion
661.01	Failure to progress
	Unspecified
	Protracted labor
763.8	Care related to or affecting fetus
662.2	Second stage
7 766.2	Postmaturity and prolonged pregnancy
	Fetal distress
768.2	before labor
768.3	during labor
650	Fetal growth retardation
	Cesarean section
656.3	fetal distress or complication
66 9.8	Forceps delivery
654.2	VBAC
654.20	unspecified delivery
654.21	with mention of antepartum condition
654.23	antepartum condition or complication
658.2	Prolonged rupture of membranes

658.20	unspecified
658.23	without mention antepartum condit
652.9	Abnormal presentation
652.90	unspecified
652.91	without mention
652.93	antepartum condit
660.33	Deep transverse arrest
659.9	Unspecified obstetrical procedure
666.24	Postpartum hemorrhage
648.80	Gestational diabetes
654.1	Fibroid in pregnancy
041.02	Beta strep
569.82	Ulcerative Colitis
651.03	Twin Pregnancy
642.40	Pregnancy Induced Hypertension
054.10	Herpes

For a complete ICD-9 codes consult the following internet site http://www-informatics.ucdavis.edu/icd9/icd9cm.html

CPT Codes

99078 Physician educational services rendered to patients in a group setting
99371 Telephone calls for consultation or medical management; simple or brief
99050 Services requested after office hours in addition to basic service
99054 Services requested on Sundays and holidays in addition to basic services
99071 Educational supplies
99499 Evaluation management service
59410 Vaginal delivery only including postpartum care
59425 Antepartum care only (4-6 visits)
59426 Seven or more visits
59430 Postpartum care only
59515 Cesarean delivery only including postpartum care

HOME MEDICAL SERVICES
    New Patient

90100	Brief visit
90115	Intermediate visit
90117	Extended visit

    Established Patient

90150	Limited visit
90160	Intermediate visit
90170	Extended visit

HOSPITAL SERVICE

90240 `	Brief visit
90250	Limited visit

90260   Intermediate visit

CONSULTATIONS (PHYSICIAN REFERRAL)
90260   New Patient
90600   Limited
90605   Intermediate
90610   Extended
90620   Comprehensive
      Established Patient
90640   Brief
90641   Limited
90642   Intermediate
90643   Extended visit

HOSPITAL MEDICAL SERVICES
      Brief History & Exam
90215   Intermediate H & P
90220   Comprehensive H & P

OFFICE MEDICAL SERVICES
      New Patient
90000   Brief visit
90010   Limited visit
90015   Intermediate visit
90017   Extended visit
      Established Patient
90030   Minimal visit
90040   Brief visit
90050   Limited visit
90060   Intermediate visit
90070   Extended visit

SPECIAL SERVICES
99014   Telephone Conference
      Night Services
99052   10p-8a
99054   Sun/Holiday Services
99056   Services at patient request location other than usual

SUPPLIES
99070   Manual breast pump
99071   Educational supplies
99155   Medical management conference

EVALUATION AND MANAGEMENT
99499   Unlisted
99078   Education Group Session

Bibliography

Advertising

Do-It-Yourself Advertising by Fred Hahn Wiley (800/225-5945)

Business

Business a to Z Source Finder: a Locator Guide to Sources for the Information Seeker by Elizabeth Louise Vandivier & Kathleen Brown
      Beacon Bay Press (410/956-6855)
Business Information: How to Find It by Michael Lavin
      Oryx Press (800/279-6799)
Business Information Sources by Lorna Daniels
      University of California Press (800/777-4726)
Dive Right In- The Sharks Won't Bite: The Entrepreneurial Woman's Guide to Success by Jane Wesman
      Upstart Publishing (800/235-8866)
Does Someone at Work Treat You Badly? By Leonard Fuller
      Putnam Berkeley Publishing Group
Encyclopedia of Business Information Sources edited by James Woy
      Gale Research, Inc. (800/877-4253)
Handbook of Business Information by Diane Wheeler Strauss
      Libraries Unlimited (800/237-6124)
How to Run a Small Business by J.K. Tax Institute
      McGraw-Hill Publishing Co. (800/262-4729)
Intelligent Business Alliances by Larraine Segil
      Times Business Books (800/733-3000)
Labor Support Forms: a Guide to Doula Charting by Cheri Grant
      M& W Productions
Managing Corporate Culture, Innovation and Intrapreneourship by Howard Oden
      Greenwood Publishing
Minding Her Own Business: The Self-Employed Woman's Guide to Taxes and Recordkeeping, by Jan Zobel, EastHill Press, Oakland, CA,1998.
The Art of Partnering: How Increase Your Profits and Enjoyment in Business Through Alliance Relationships by Edwin Richard Rigsbee
      Kendall Hunt Publishing (805/371-4636)
The Coming of Age of Executive Women by Dawn-Marie Driscoll & Carol Godlberg, The Free Press, a division of Macmillan, Inc.
The Female Entrepreneur by Connie Sitterly
      Crisp Publications (800/442-7477)
The Frugal Entrepreneur by Terri Lonier
      Portico Press (800/222-7656)

The McGraw-Hill Guide to Starting Your Own Business by Steven Harper
    McGraw-Hill

The Seasons of Business by Judith Waldrop
    American Demographic Books (800/828-1133)
The Successful Business Plan: Secrets & Strategies by Rhonda Abrams
    The Oasis Press (800/228-2275)

Communication

Communication Focus Issue No. 22, Vol IX
    North American Management Press
Constructive Conflict Management: Managing to Make a Difference by John
    Crawley, Nicholas Bradley Publishing, London (800/533-0301)
Competence-Based Employment Interviewing by Jeffrey Berman
    Greenwood Publishing
Difficult People by Roberta Cava
    Firefly Books (800/387-5085)
*Making the Patient Your Partner: Communication Skills for Doctors and Other
    Caregivers* by Thomas Gordon
    Greenwood Publishing
Mastering Change by Mark Sanborn
    Career Track Publishing
*Powerful Telephone Skills: A Quick and Handy Guide for Any Manager or
Business Owner* by the editors of Career Press
    Career Press (800/227-3371)
TeamWork: What Must Go Right, What Can Go Wrong by Carl E. Larson &
Frank LaFasto
    Sage Publications
*Teaming Up: Making the Transition To a Self-Directed, Team Based
Organization* by Darrel Ray & Howard Bronstein
    McGraw-Hill
Telephone Skills from A to Z by Nancy Friedman
    Crisp Publications (800/892-9911)
*Winning Telephone Tips: 30 Fast and Profitable Tips for Making the Best Use of
Your Phone* by Paul Timm
    Career Press (800/227-3371)

Computer

1997 Guide to Intranets in Health Care edited by Jeff Muscarella
    Faulkner & Gray, Inc. (800/535-8403)
Point & Click Business Builder by Seth Godin
    Upstart (800/245-2665)

Financial

Bootstrapper's Success Secrets: 151 Tactics for Building Your Business on a Shoestring Budget by Kimberly Stansell
        Career Press (800/227-3371)

Grant Writing

Enterprise in the Nonprofit Sector by James Crimmins & Mary Keil
        Partners for Livable Places, Washington DC
Getting Funded: a Complete Guide to Proposal Writing by Mary Hall
        Continuing Education Publications, Portland, Oregon
Grant Money & How to Get It by Richard Boss
        RR Bowler Co., New York
Grant Proposals that Succeeded by Virginia White
        Plenum Press, New York
Guidelines for Preparing Proposals: a manual on how to organize winning proposals for grants, venture capital, R&D projects, other proposals by Roy Meador
        Lewis Publishers, Chelsea, Michigan
Guidelines for Preparing the Research Proposal by John Behling
        University Press of America, Maryland
Plain Talk about Grants by Robert Geller
        California State Library Foundation, Sacramento, California
Proposal Preparation by Rodney Stewart
        Wiley, New York
The Basic Handbook of Grants Management by Robert Lefferts
        Prentice Hall, New Jersey
The "How To" Grants Manual: Successful Techniques for Obtaining Public and Private Grants by David Bauer
        American Council on Education, New York
Writing Grant Proposals that Win
        Capitol Publications (800/221-0425)
Writing that Research Proposal edited by Victor Campbell
        American Association of Critical Care Nurses, Newport Beach, California

Home-Based Business

Complete Idiot's Guide to Starting a Home-Based Business Barbara Weltman
        Alpha Books
How Raise a Family and a Career Under One Roof by Lisa Roberts
        Brookhaven Press (800/782-7424)
Mompreneurs: A Mother's Practical Step-by-Step Guide to Work-at-Home Success by Ellen Parlapiano & Patricia Cobe
        Perigee Books (800/631-8571)

Honey, I want to Start My Own Business by Azriela Jaffe
　　Harper Business (800/331-3761)
The Family Manager's Guide to Working Moms by Kathy Peel
　　Ballantine Books (800/726-0600)
The Home Office and Small Business Answer Book by Janet Attard
　　Henry Holt Publishers
When Mothers Work by Joan Peters
　　Addison-Wesley (800/822-6339)

Job Transition

Job Shift: How Prosper in a Workplace Without Jobs by William Bridges
　　(Addison-Wesley)
Quality Connection by Institute for Healthcare Improvement
　　(IHI 617/754-4800)
Zen and the Art of Making a Living by Laurence G. Boldt (Arkana, 1993)
How to Find the Work You Love by Laurence G. Boldt (Arkana, 1996)

Leadership

The Manager's Short Course: a Complete Course in Leadership Skills for the First-Time Manager by Bill & Char Holton
　　John Wiley & Sons (800/225-5945)

Legalities

An Ounce of Prevention: Marketing, Sales and Advertising Law for Non-Lawyers by Steven Meyerowitz
　　Visible Ink Press (800/877-4253)
The Employer's Legal Handbook by Fred Steingold (Nolo Press)
　　Nolo Press (1-800-992-6656)
The Complete Book of Legal Forms by Daniel Sitarz
　　Nova Publishing (800/748-1175)

Managed Care

The Managed Care 1500: a Complete Guide to the Most Influential Managed Care Leaders and Organizations in the United States by Faulkner & Gray Healthcare Information Center
　　(Faulkner & Gray 800/535-8403)

Marketing

1,000+ Stationery Designs: Instant Image Design Guide by Val Cooper

(Point Pacific Press/800-896-2341)

Do It Yourself Advertising and Promotion: How to Produce Great Ads, Brochures, Catalogs, Direct Mail, Web Sites, and Much More by Fred Hahn & Kenneth Mangun(John Wiley & Sons)

CyberMarketing by Len Keeler, Amacom (800/262-9699)

Do-It-Yourself Marketing by David Ramacitti,(AMACOM)

Ethics and Manipulation in Advertising by Michael Phillips,Greenwood Publishing

Getting the Most From Your Yellow Page Advertising by Barry Maher, (Warner)

Grow Your Business with Desktop Marketing by Steve Morgenstern,(Random House)

Guerrilla Marketing Online by Jay Conrad Levinson & Charles Rubin Houghton Mifflin (800/225-3362)

How to Get Your Point Across in 30 Seconds or Less by Milo O. Frank (Simon & Schuster)

How to Make Your Advertising Make Money by John Caples (Prentice-Hall)

Making Marketing Manageable: a Painless and Practical Guide to Self Promotion by Ilise Benun(F&W Publications 800/737-0783)

Marketing on the Internet by Michael Mathiesen,,Maximum Press (800/989-6733)

Marketing Your Services: For People Who Hate to Sell by Rick Crandall (Contemporary Books 312/540-4500)

On the Air by Al Parinello

Online Marketing Handbook by Daniel Janal, Van Nostrand (800/842-3636)

The Do-able Marketing Plan: Business Survival and Growth for the '90s and Beyond by Adrienne Zoble,   (Adrienne Zoble Associates 800/685-8333)

Walk Your Talk: Growing Your Business Faster Through Successful Cross-Promotional Partnerships by Karen Anderson, Spiral Publishing (800/488-KAREN)

Medical Care

Patient Centered Medicine: A Professional Evolution. Center for Research in Medical Education and Health Care, Philadelphia, Pennsylvania

Through a Patient's Eyes: Understanding and Promoting Patient Centered Care. The Pickering Institute, Boston, Massachusetts

"Providers Look to Industry for Quality Models", *Modern Healthcare*. 18(29):24-32.

Non-Profit

Grant Thorton LLP. *Serving on the Board of a Tax-Exempt Organization*, Grant Thorton LLP, 1995

Software

ActionPlus Contact Suite 2.51 by Warever (800/766-7229) is a staff scheduler that helps you set the dates and times for meetings, assign employees to specific clients and manage vacation time.

Billing Solution 2.0 by Pro Venture (800/325-3508) handles all aspects of a business billing cycle, including estimates, invoices, and late-payment tracking.

Decisive Survey 2.0 by Decisive Technologies (800/987-9995) is designed to gather and analyze electronic questionnaires via return mail or your website.

Do-It-Yourself Advertising by Adams Media (800/872-5627) teaches you how to design and execute a marketing campaign.

Form Magic by New England Business Service, Inc.(800/367-6327) automatically generates forms such as proposals, invoices, checks, purchase orders and more.

FrontPage is an easy-to-use application that lets you design and manage your web site.

Marketing Builder by Jian (800/346-5426) is a project-specific sales and marketing program with text and spreadsheet templates.

Marketing Plus 2.2 by Palo Alto Software (800/229-7526) is a complete marketing program, not just a set of templates.

People Scheduler 3.0 by Adaptiv Software (800/598-1222) not only handles staff scheduling but keeps track of employee profiles, hourly wage rates, time away from office, and attendance.

Small Business Lawyer by McGraw Hill (800/2MCGRAW) contains more than 300 forms and business agreements.

Softfind by World Class software (800/270-2172) has hundreds of business software demos that you can search by industry or by application.

Survey+ 2.2 by AutoData Systems (662-2192) has several ready-made surveys to use or edit.

The Complete Book of Small Business Legal Forms by Nova Publishing (800/748-1175) includes 125 standard legal documents.

The Right Site by American Demographic Inc. (800/828-1133) gives demographic information on geographic areas by county, ZIP code, metro area or TV market.

Timeslips Deluxe 8.0 by Timeslips (800/285-0999) may be difficult to use but is one of the most popular time and billing package on the market.

Time and Profit 2.01 by BytePro (800/713-5322) simplifies invoicing by combining four applications in one task and activity time billing, scheduling, contact management, and double-entry accounting.

Total E-Call by American Network Systems, Inc. (800/441-3875) combines telephone, Internet, e-mail and record-keeping features.

Visual Staff Scheduler 3.0 by Atlas Business solutions (800/874-8801) can lay out and print up to 42 days of scheduling information on a single sheet of paper.

10 Million U.S. Businesses by American Information, Inc. (800/624-0076) gives key statistics on 10 million national businesses.

URL's Of Interest to Doula Programs

Information on the Internet
www.inet-images.com/Creative/help.html
> for the Internet novice about basic Internet knowledge

www.Four11.com/
> database of e-mail addresses and home pages
> register your e-mail address

wwli.com/translation/netglos/netglos.html
> a glossary of Internet terms in multiple languages

www.mit.edu:8001/people/mkgray/moved.html/autopilot.html
> a random web page generator that uses Netscape's "pull"
> technology so that every 12 seconds a new web site appears on
> screen

www.hotwired.com
> one of the first Net magazines

www.novator.com/remind/remind.html
> an Internet reminder service

www.vocaltec.com/demo11.htm
> download a free demo of the Internet Phone

www.oise.on.ca/~jnorris/nursenet/sparks.html
> Susan Spark's Cybertutorial

newwindPub.com/medguide/
> Michael Hogarth's Internet Guide for Health Professionals

ua1vm.ua.edu/~crispen/roadmap.html
> Patrick Crispen's Roadmap

Search Engines
altavista.digital. Com
> AltaVista
> a "must visit" site; rated by Internet World as providing the most
> comprehensive results

www.excite.com
> Excite

www.lycos.com
> Lycos; one of the oldest search engines

www.metacrawler.com
> Metacrawler Parallel Web Search

www.yahoo.com
> Yahoo; rated by Internet World as the largest and most popular directory

guide.infoseek.com
> Infoseek; rated by Internet World as providing the most relevant
> results

www.webcrawler.com
> Web Crawler; quick searches but definitely "no-frills"

www.opentext.com:8080
>   Opentext; rated by Internet World as the best designed search site
>   on the Internet

inktomi.berkeley.edu/query.html
>   Inktomi

www.cs.colorado.edu/wwww/
>   WWW Worm; one of the pioneers of web-searching tools

www.search.com
>   incorporates web indexes such as AltaVista, Lycos, InfoSeek and
>   Excite

Abuse

www.cs.utk.edu/~bartley/saInfoPage.html
>   The Sexual Assault Information Page Electronic Newsletter

www.ajn.org/mcn/5.9/m509252e.lt
>   an article on helping survivors of sexual abuse through labor

Addiction

www.moscow.com/Resources/SelfHelp/AA/
>   Alcoholics Anonymous

Birth

www.childbirth.org/CEP.html
>   web site for Cutting Edge Press
>   information regarding birth related material and products for
>   doulas, midwives, nurses, etc.

www.childbirth.org
>   one of the most comprehensive maternity related sites

www.well.com
>   web site for The Farm in Summertown, Tennessee

www.alace.org
>   web page of the Association of Labor Assistants and Childbirth
>   Educators

www.efn.org/~djz/birth/birthindex.html
>   web page of Midwifery Today

www.fensende.com
>   web site by midwife/doulas regarding birth
>   information on *Birth and Babies*, the new quarterly journal for the
>   natural childbirth educator

www.homefirst.com
>   information regarding home birth and home birth services in the
>   Chicago area

www.efn.org/~djz/birth/birthibdex.html
>   Online Birth Center information on midwifery and natural childbirth

www.efn.org/~djz/birth/homebirth.html

Windsong Midwifery's materials for midwives
(handouts, client/midwife forms, midwife protocols, etc.)
Many materials are available on disk

www.ghc.org/
information from Group Health Cooperative on various birth related
topics

www.noah.cuny.edu/pregnancy/pregnancy.html
part of New York Online Access to Health

www.wrsgroup.com
web site for Childbirth Graphics

www.storksite.com
provides answers to pregnancy and childbirth related questions
from an experienced perinatal nurse and educator, reference
library, and links to other sites

www.calpoly.edu/~dfrieda/mazeltov/index.html
web site for LaMazeltov

ourworld.compus.homepages/romabirth/use.htm
information on the ROMA birth wheel equipment

dialspace.dial.pipex.com/danny.tucker/
web site for an obstetrician in Great Britain

oncolink.upenn.edu/disease/breast/pregnancy.html
information for women who have breast cancer and are pregnant

www.parentsplace.com/peterson/healing.html
an article by Gayle Peterson on counseling as a tool to unlocking
the door to healing

www.gatech.edu/nar/win95/shira.html
an article on women and obstetrics and the loss of childbirth to
male physicians

www.olen.com
Olen Pregnancy Calendar

www.efn.org/~djz
Midwifery Today

www.itp.tsoa.nyu.edu//alumni/birthmessages
Birth Messages chapter from Birth As An American Rite of Passage
by Robbie Davis-Floyd

Breastfeeding

www2.islandnet.com/~bedford/brstfeed.html
The Breastfeeding Page

www.clark.net/pubactivist/bfpage/bfpage.html
Breastfeeding Advocacy Page

www.lalecheleague.org
Mother-to-mother breastfeeding support and information

Business

www.smalloffice.com

>   web site for the magazines *Home Office Computing* and *Small Business Computing*
>
>   weekly hardware and software picks, up-to-date information from Capitol Hill regarding small business issues, and links to sites for home-based small and business owners

www2.switchboard.com

>   free nationwide residential and business directory

www.omicronet.com

>   a consortium of corporations that are dedicated to improving the value of technology to business

www.mmm.com/psnotes

>   download a free 30-day sample of the Post-It note software

www.sbaonline.gov

>   Small Business Association's web site

www.irs.utreas.gov

>   comprehensive information about small business tax topics, filing services, and forms

www.petersons.com

>   the ins and outs of effective small business political activism

www.esselte.com

>   online magazine for small and home offices

www.washingtonpost.com/parachute

>   advice from Dick Bolles regarding resumes, job counseling, etc.

www.ups.com

>   United Parcel Service will accept same-day package pickup requests via this web site

www.the-dma.org

>   tips, trends and information from the Direct Marketing Association

www.access.gpo.gov/su_docs/

>   information on government databases, regulations, laws from the Government Printing Office

www.usedmall.com

>   if you want to buy or sell used or surplus equipment

www.pitt.edu/~malhotra/interest.html

>   a meta-index of more than 2,500 web sites on contemporary business, management and technology issues

www.wilsonweb.com/articles/web-do.htm

>   an article on what a web site can do for your business

Death and Dying

www.hospicefoundation.org

>   information on comfort and support for those in the final days of a fatal illness

www.hospicefoundaton.org
> The Hospice Foundation's site to help patients and their families

Government

www.nlm.nih.gov
> Agency for Health Policy and Research

www.fda.gov/fdahomepage.html
> US Food & Drug Administration

www.os.dhhs.gov/progorg/progorg/html
> Department of Health and Human Services

policy.net/capweb/congress.html
> CapWeb: A Guide to Congress

www.os.dhhs.gov/progorg/progorg.html
> Department of Health and Human Services

www.who.ch/
> World Health Organization

www.geocities.com/CapitolHill/1007
> a way to let your elected representatives in Washington know what you

think

www.irs.ustreas.gov
> up to date information about small business topics, filing services, etc.

www.access.gpo.gov/su_docs/
> Governement Printing Office; regulations, laws, etc.

Healthcare Information

www.ama-assn.org/aps/amahg.html
> provides information on virtually every licensed physician in the US

www.bluecares.com
> web site for Blue Cross Blue Shield
> a comprehensive tour of the human body, what's new in health
> care, and links to other health related sites

www.healthgate.com
> a search engine for free access to Medline

www.HIVpositive.com
> AIDs related information

www.healthy.net
> alternative medicine

hotwired.com
> includes a health channel that features a alternative medicine clinic

www.medscape.com
> offers unlimited free access to Medline

www.medscape.com/home/MedPulse.html
> fee weekly e-mail newsletter

www.slackinc.com/matrix

Medical Matrix-Internet Clinical Medicine Resource Guide
users.aimnet.com/~hyperion/meno/menotimes.index.html
a quarterly electronic journal for alternative choices to menopause
and osteoporosis
biomed.nus.sg/kh/
Singapore medical web site
www.bcm.tmc.edu
Baylor College of Medicine web site that includes interesting
ob/gyn case studies and links to other women's health sites
www.medaccess.com
medical information
www.nci.nih.gov/
web site for the National Cancer Institute
www.dodgenet.com/nocancer
People Against Cancer gives information on nontoxic and innovative
treatment options
medinfo.org
medical information
www.nnlm.nih.gov/pnr/uwmhg/index.html
medicinal plants
www.redcross.org
The Red Cross and its programs
www.nlm.nih.gov
National Library of Medicine
www.latex.org
Delaware Valley Latex Allergy Support Network; support group
www.latexallergyhelp.com
Education for latex Allergies Support Team and Information coalition
www.modernhealthcare.com
Modern Healthcare magazine
www.yahoo.com/health
Yahoo Health Directory
healthy.net
Health World
www.visesandvirtues.com
health forum
www.ama-assn.org/aps/amahg.html
Physician Select provides information on licensed physicians
www.nlm.nih.gov/extramural_research.dir/visible_human.html
National Library of Medicine Visible Human Project
www.cdc.gov/cdc.html
CDC
www.healthweek.com
Nursing and Allied Healthweek homepage

pharminfo.com/
    Pharmaceutical Information Network
www.cuberport.net/mmg/homepage.html
    Medical Multimedia Group creates interactive software for patient
    education
www.medaccess.com
    Medaccess
www.foobar.co.uk/users/umba/stress/
    one of the top 125 web sites worldwide
    facts on stress and how to manage it
www.medinfo.org
    Medinfo
www.healthgate.com
    a search engine for free access to Medline
www.nnlm.nlm.nih.gov/pnr/uwmhg/index.html
    information about medicinal plants from the University of Washington
www.medscape.com
    unlimited free access to Medline
www.adworks.com/dizzy/vestib.html
    coping with dizziness
www.internetdatabase.com/subtopic/medicine.htm
    medicine sites
www.ketthealth.com
    a hospital-based doula site

Legal
www.law.cornell.edu/
    Cornell University's legal information
www.findlaw.com/
www.gsu.edu/~lawadim/gsulaw.html
    index for legal research
www.law.indiana.edu/
    Indiana University's virtual law site
www.fjc.gov
    The Federal Judicial Center

Marketing
www.wilsonweb.com
    sign up for a free electronic newsletter at the Web Marketing Ifo Center
www.iocom.be/pilot/cybermaarkeeting/
    mareketing terms and information

Mental Health
www.mentalhealth.com/p.html

Internet Mental Health; information on research & treatment of depression
www.cmhc.com
Mental Health Net; treatment of depression
www.coil.com/~grohol/
Psych Central

Nursing
www.odyssee.net/~fnord/nurselink.html
web pages that identifies the coolest sites of interest to nurses
www.nurseweek.com
web site for NurseWeek magazine and links to other nursing sites
users.aol.com/NsgHistory/Index.html
web site for the Association for the History of Nursing
users.twave.net/texican/
weird nursing tales
www.nurseweek.com/medmod.html
an article on nursing and its relationship to medicine
www.ajn.org
American Journal of Nursing
www.wp.com/InterNurse/letters.html
www.nih.gov/ninr
National Institute of Nursing Research
www.nursing.ab.umd.edu/students/~snewbol/
Susan Newbold's web page with links to other nursing sites
www,odyssee.net/~fnord/nurselink.html
links to coolest sites on the web of interest to nurses

Nutrition
www2.hunterlink.net.au/~ddnaw/Vegan_Pages/
information for vegans
www.honors.indiana.edu/~veggie/recipes.cgi
vegetarian and vegan recipes and open forum
www.hoptechno.com/rdindex.htm
on-line nutrition advice by a registered dietician
vm.cfsan.fda.gov/list.html
web site for the FDA Center for Food Safety & Applied Nutrition
www.fatfree.com/usda/usda.cgi
a user-friendly, searchable database on USDA nutrient values
www.geocities.com/RodeoDrive/1154
The Vegetarian Youth Network, a website run by teens for teens

Organizations
users.aol.com/NsgHistory/Index.html
American Association for the History of Nursing

www.ahima.org
   American Health Information Management Association
www.apta.org
   American Physical Therapy Association
www.alpha.org/
   American Public Health Association
www.redcross.org
   American Red Cross
www.alace.org/atrain.html

Resources

American Academy of Husband-
Coached Childbirth
PO Box 5224
Sherman Oaks, CA 91413
800/423-2397

American Baby
475 Park Ave. South
NY, NY 10016
800/368-7899
free subscriptions for childbirth
educators and those that work with
maternity clients

American College of Obstetricians and
Gynecologists
409 12th Street SW
Washington, DC 20024
202/638-5577

ASPO/Lamaze International
1200 19th St. NW
Suite 300
Washington, DC 20036
800/368-4404

Association of Childbirth Educators
and Labor Assistants
P.O. Box 382724
Cambridge, MA 02238-2724
617/441-2500

BIRTH
Blackwell Scientific Publications
238 Main Street
Cambridge, MA 02142
617/876-7000

Birthworks
42 Tallowood Dr.
Medford, NJ 08055
609/953-9380

Cascade Healthcare Products
141 Commercial St. NE
Salem, OR 97301
800/443-9942

C. F. E., Inc.
415 Bauxhall
Katy, TX 77450-2203
281/497-8894
http://www.childbirth.org/CFE.html
information on labor assistants, doula
training and referrals

Childbirth Enhancement Foundation
1004 George Ave.
Rockledge, FL 32955
407/631-9977

Childbirth Forum
Ontarget Media
1444 I St. NW
Washington, DC 20005
202/296-1850

Childbirth Instructor
52 Vanderbilt Ave
Suite 501
NY, NY 10017
212/986-1422

Cutting Edge Press
415 Bauxhall
Katy, TX 77450-2203
281/497-8894
http://www.childbirth.org/CEP.html
maternity related books and products
doula supplies
complete inventory of Childbirth
Graphics materials

Doulas of North America
110 23rd Ave. East
Seattle, WA 98112
206/325-1419
ASKDONA@aol.com

International Cesarean Awareness
Network
1304 Kingsdale Ave.
Redondo Beach, CA 90278
310/542-5368

International Childbirth Education
Association
P.O. Box 20048
Minneapolis, MN 55420-0048
800/624-4934

International Lactation Consultant
Association
P.O. Box 4031
University of Virginia Station
Charlottesville, VA 22903
404/381-5127

Labor Support Association and
Registry
Ontario, Canada
905/829-3385

La Leche League International
1400 N. Meacham Rd.
Schaumburg, IL 60173-4840 USA
847/519-9585
847/519-0035 fax
www.lalecheleague.org/

Lamaze Baby
Lamaze Publishing Co.
9 Old Kings's Highway South
Darien, CT 06820
800/832-0277

Midwifery Today
P.O. Box 2672
Eugene, OR 97402
800/743-0974

M&W Productions
P.O. Box 14003
Tulsa, Oklahoma 74159
918/288-7667

Seattle Midwifery School
2524 16th Ave. South
Room 300
Seattle, WA 98144
206/322-8834